my Early MATHS Workbook

Some Are Lost

Look at the picture given below. Count from 1-10. Some numbers are missing. What are they?

3   7

6   10   2

4   9

Write the missing numbers in the blank space.

Date: _____   Teacher's Signature: _____

Fun with Zero

Zero is an important number in maths. Put a zero in front of every number and see a new, bigger number.

10

2

5

3

20

Date: _____

Teacher's Signature: _____

Count the number of fingers held up in the hands below. Circle the correct match with number 4.

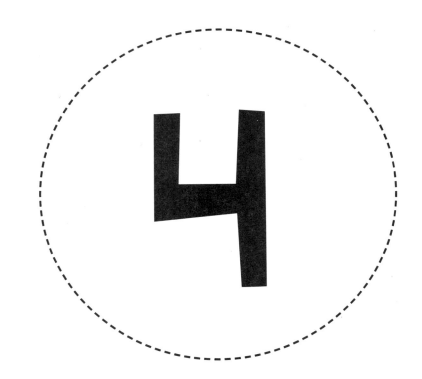

Date: _____   Teacher's Signature: _____

Oliya, the Octopus

How many arms does Oliya, the octopus, have? Count and write.

Oliya, the octopus, has ___ arms.

Now trace the number 8.

8

Date: _____   Teacher's Signature: _____

Compare Us

Look at the images and tick (✓) the correct answer in each of the following.

1. Which is the baby goat?

2. Which radish is thinner?

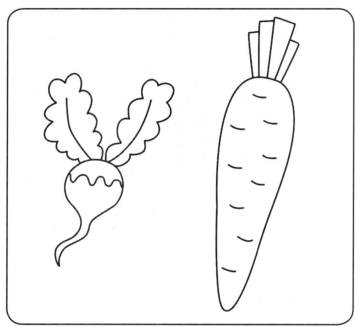

3. Which flower is the tallest?

4. Which is the smallest object?

Colour the parrots with the number 10.

I Live Under Water

Look at the following pictures carefully and colour the animals that live in water. Also, count their number and write it in the box given below.

Hidden Number

Look at the given pictures carefully. There are some numbers hidden in the pictures. Locate and encircle them.

The Sun and the Moon

Look at the pictures given below. They are made of different types of lines. Choose and tick (✓) the correct answer.

slanting lines ☐

curved lines ☐

straight lines ☐

slanting lines ☐

curved lines ☐

straight lines ☐

Baby Animals

Look at the picture given below carefully. Count and write the number of puppies.

The number of puppies is _____.

Write the names of six other baby animals.

1. _____   2. _____

3. _____   4. _____

5. _____   6. _____

My Birthday Candles

How old are you? Colour the number of candles according to your age.

Example: Colour 5 candles if you are 5 years old.

Date: _____

Teacher's Signature: _____

Who Am I?

Read the clues, identify the names of the little tiger cubs, and then write their names below them.

Browny is the only one sitting among Theo and Naughty.

Theo has big eyes.

_____

_____   _____

Date: _____   Teacher's Signature: _____

Baby Dinos

Colour and count the number of baby dinos.

Date: _____

Teacher's Signature: _____

Biggest to Smallest

Number the things from biggest to smallest according to their sizes. Number the biggest object 4 and smallest object 1.

Balloons in a Bunch

Put a number on every balloon starting from 1.

Find out how many balloons are there in the bunch?

Date: _____

Teacher's Signature: _____

Trace and Colour

Trace the numbers and colour the picture with your favourite colours.

Date: _____

Teacher's Signature: _____

Flower Counting

Look at the picture given below carefully and then fill in the blanks that follow.

Count and write the total number of all flowers. _____

Count and write the total number of roses. _____

Count and write the total number of lotuses. _____

Big and Small

Colour the largest bee red and the smallest bee blue. Colour the bee with the greatest number green and colour the bee with the smallest number yellow.

Colour the Flags

Count and colour the flags given below.

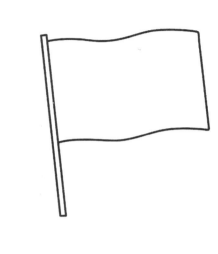
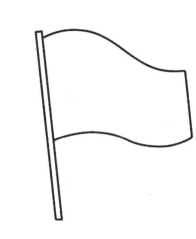

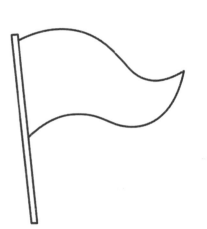
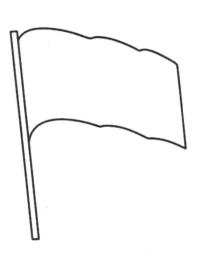

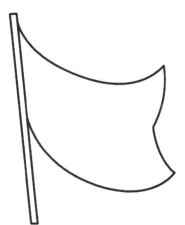

Date: _____

Teacher's Signature: _____

Colour five scoops in each ice cream cone with your favourite colour.

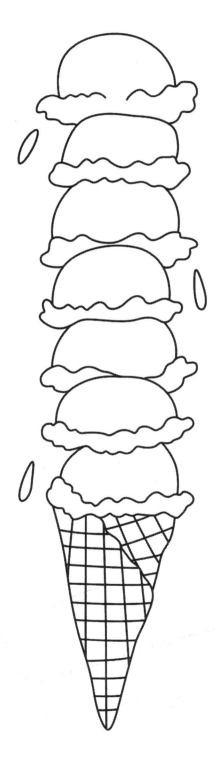

Date: _____

Teacher's Signature: _____

Smallest and Tallest

Write 'T' in front of the tallest block tower and 'S' in front of the shortest block tower.

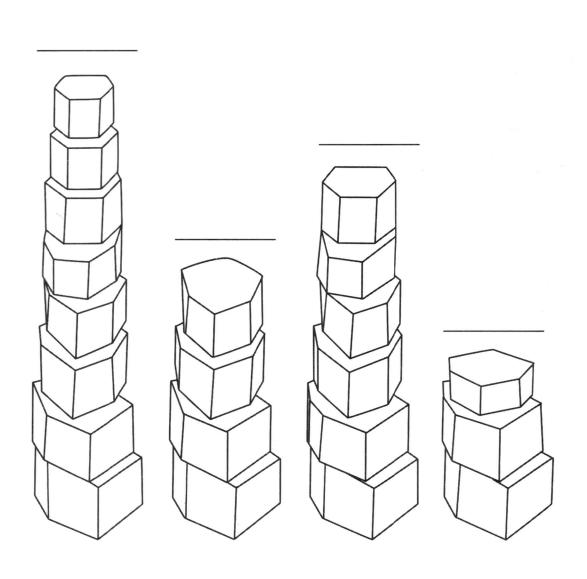

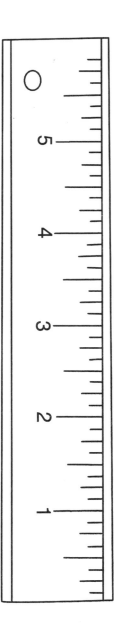

Date: _____   Teacher's Signature: _____

I Am Number 8

What's hiding in Number 8? Colour the spaces in which number 8 is written to find out the hidden fruits.

The fruits hidden in number 8 are _____.

Date: _____   Teacher's Signature: _____

Two-Digit Numbers

Circle the hidden two-digit numbers in the following objects.

Date: _____

Teacher's Signature: _____

Count and Colour

Colour the flowers as per the instructions given below.

First three flowers: **Red**

Next four flowers: **Pink**

Next two flowers: **Yellow**

Remaining three flowers: **Blue**

Date: _____   Teacher's Signature: _____

Who Am I?

Look at the pictures given below and identify them with the help of the Clue Box.

_____

_____

_____

CLUE BOX

zebra	giraffe	horse

Who is the tallest among them? _____

In the Sky

Trace the shapes and write the number of moons and stars.

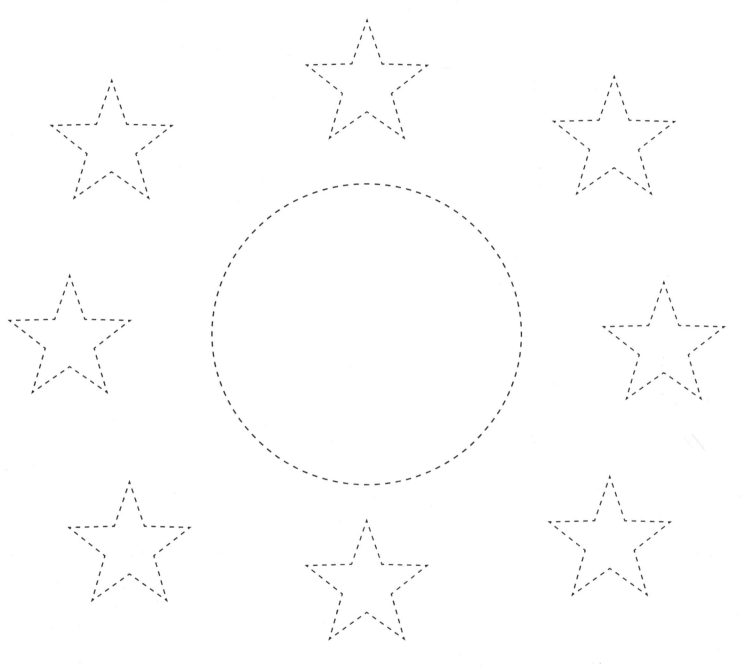

Number of moons _____.

Number of stars _____.

Kite and the Colours

Colour the kite according to the Colour Key.

		Colour Key		
1 = purple	2 = red	3 = blue	4 = yellow	5 = green

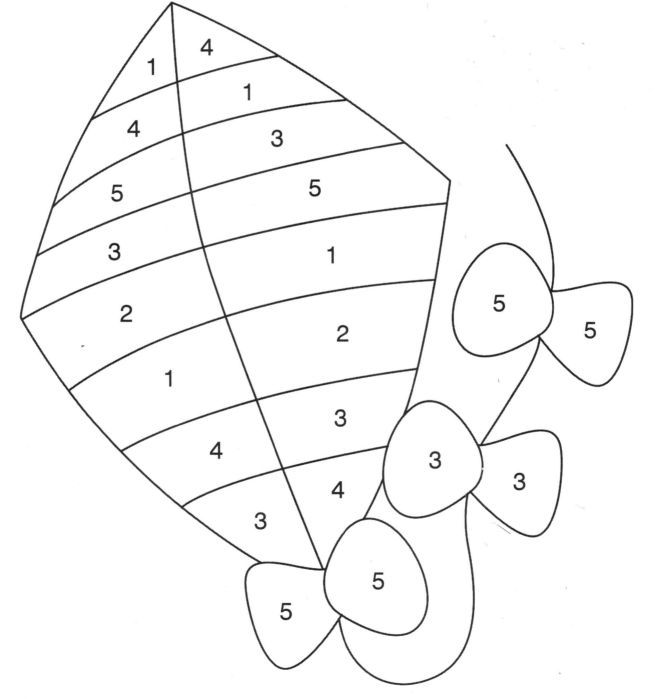

Count the Shapes

Count the number of shapes in each row. Colour the shape or shapes new to you.

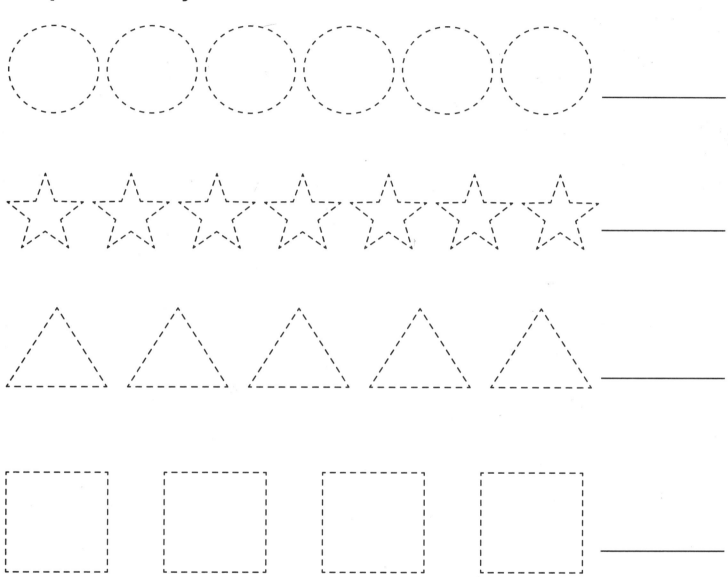

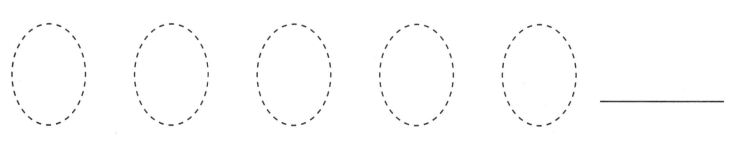

A Collection

How many types of objects are there in the box? _____

Date: _____   Teacher's Signature: _____

Trace the number 9.

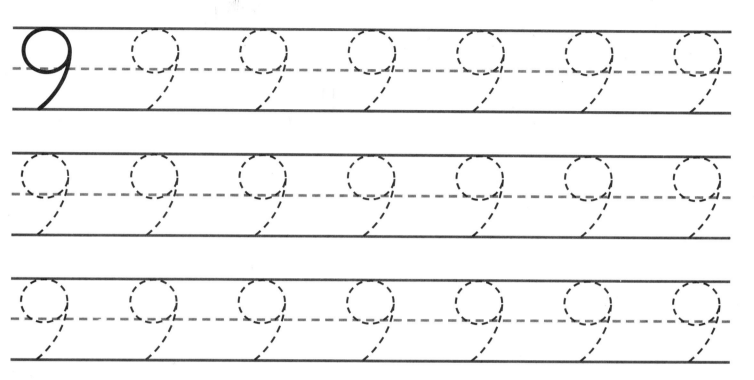

Colour the following pictures. In each picture, a number is hidden. Can you find that number?

Hidden number in the pictures is _____.

My Body Parts

Look at the images given below. Match the body parts with their correct numbers in our body.

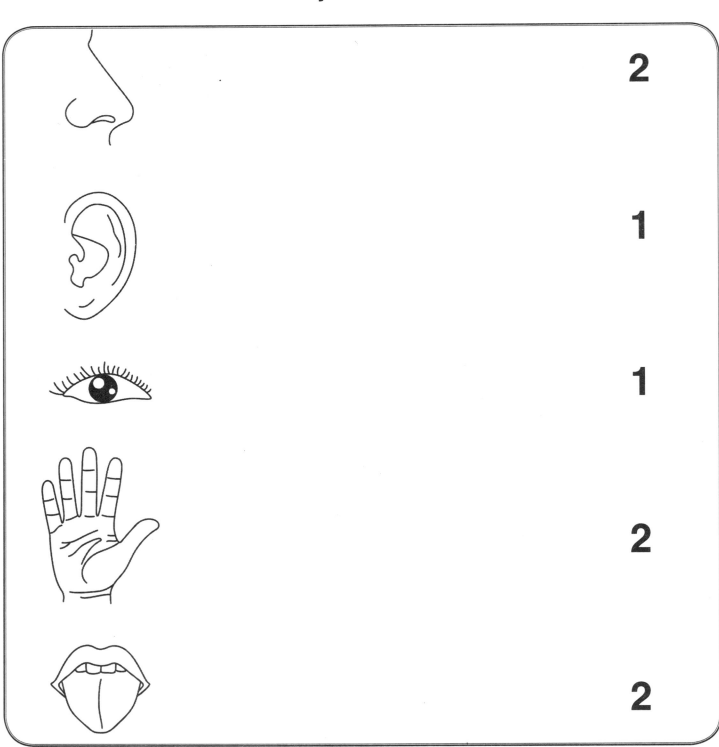

Date: _____

Teacher's Signature: _____

I Am the Tallest

Look at the images given below. These are of different sizes. Circle the tallest one in each of the following.

Date: _____

Teacher's Signature: _____

Colour by the Number

Colour all the spaces with the number 1 RED

Colour all the spaces with the number 2 YELLOW

Colour all the spaces with the number 3 BLUE

Colour all the spaces with the number 4 BROWN

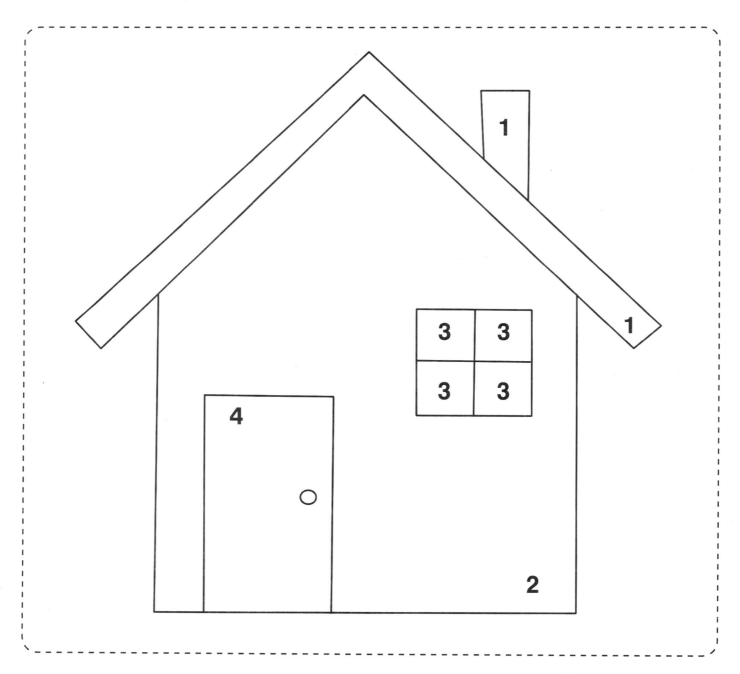

Date: _____

Teacher's Signature: _____

Put in Right Order

Arrange the drawing sequence correctly by numbering them. Also colour the complete drawing.

Count and Complete

Look at the image given below carefully and then count and complete the following story.

I am a little lamb. My name is Kit.

I have _____ ears.

I have _____ legs.

I have _____ nose.

I have _____ eyes.

I have _____ tail.

Date: _____

Teacher's Signature: _____

Colour By Numbers

Follow the Colour Key and complete the activity.

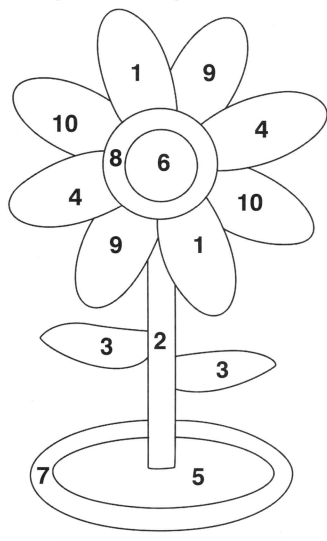

Colour Key

1 = Pink   2 = Green

3 = Gray   4 = Dark Pink

5 = Purple   6 = Yellow

7 = Red   8 = Maroon

9 = Blue   10 = Sky Blue

I Am the Shortest!

Circle the tower, which is the shortest in each pair.

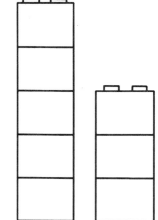

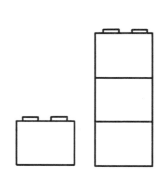

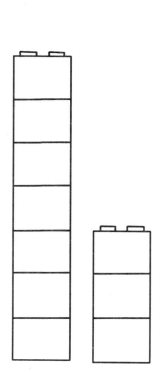

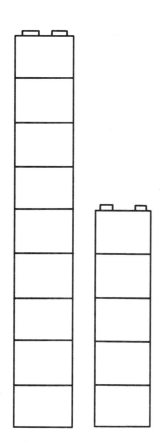

Date: _____

Teacher's Signature: _____

Count and Match

Count and match the following. One has been done for you.

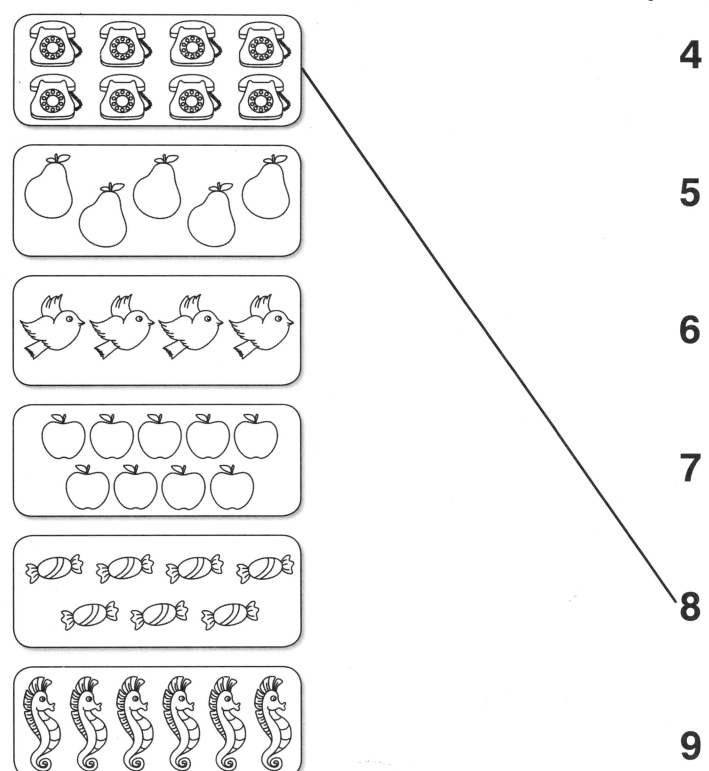

4

5

6

7

8

9

Which Is the Largest?

Circle the largest picture in each row with a red crayon.

Date: _____

Teacher's Signature: _____

Number Fun

Some numbers are hidden in the images given below. Find the numbers and write in the boxes given below them.

Hidden Animal

Colour the number 4 and see which animal is hidden there.

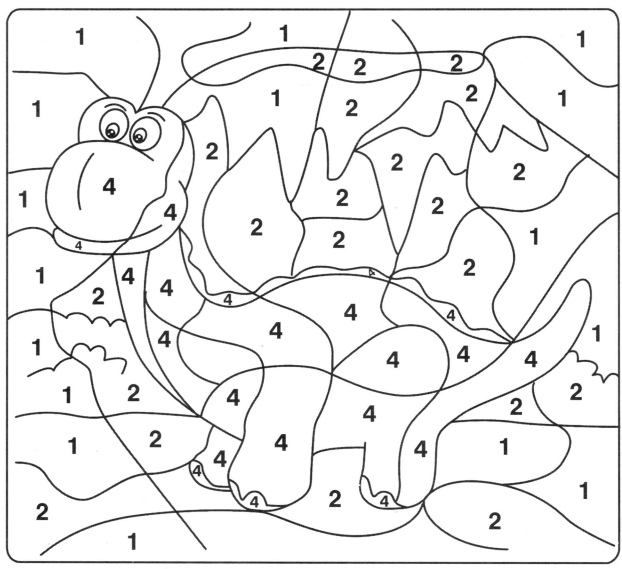

Date: _____

Teacher's Signature: _____

Busy Bee

Colour the bees according to the instructions.

Wings with no. 0 = Yellow   Wings with no. 1 = Red

Wings with no. 2 = Green   Wings with no. 3 = Blue

Bodies and antennas = Brown

Panda Food

Mamma panda and baby panda want to eat fresh grass. Help them reach the grass by following the numbers starting from 1.

Date: _____   Teacher's Signature: _____

Join the Dots

Join the dots from 1-10 to complete the picture and colour it.

Date: _____   Teacher's Signature: _____

Who Is Small?

Look at the objects in each box and circle the smaller ones.

Date: _____

Teacher's Signature: _____

Pups and Kittens

The pups and the kittens are playing together. Look at them and answer the following questions.

The number of pups is _____.

The number of kittens is_____.

I Love Circles

Colour all the circular objects.

Date: _____

Teacher's Signature: _____

My Uncle's Farm

My uncle has six sheep in his farm.

One day  more baby sheep came there.

How many sheep are there now?

Date: _____   Teacher's Signature: _____

Fruits and Vegetables

Ella's mother went to the market and bought many fruits and vegetables. Look at them and answer the questions that follow.

How many types of vegetables did Ella's mother buy?

Ella's mother bought _____ vegetables.

How many types of fruits did Ella's mother buy?

Ella's mother bought _____ fruits.

Baby Bears

Identify the baby bears and write the total number of baby bears in all the pictures.

Date: _____

Let's Count and Add

Count and add the objects and then write their total number in the given boxes.

1.  +  =

2.  + 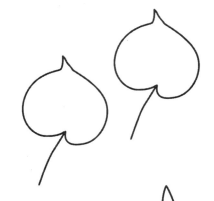 =

3.  + 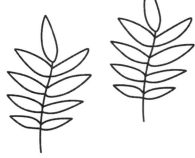 =

4.  +  =

Date: _____   Teacher's Signature: _____

Zoo Time!

Emily went to the zoo. She saw so many animals there. Look at them and answer the questions that follow.

How many rabbits are there?

How many hippos are there?

How many squirrels are there?

How many bears are there?

Heavier or Lighter

Compare the pictures in each box and then write 'Heavier' or 'Lighter' below them accordingly.

Kelly and Elly

Kelly and Elly are two fishes. They mixed their sets of buckets and shovels. Draw a line to match the buckets and shovels that have the same pattern.

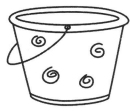

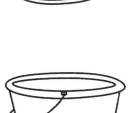

Date: _____

Teacher's Signature: _____

I Am Yellow in Colour

Colour and count the following fruits and circle the ones that are yellow in colour.

How many fruits will be left in the box if you remove all the yellow fruits?

_____

Date: _____

Teacher's Signature: _____

How Many?

Look at the pictures given below and answer the questions that follow.

How many butterflies are there in the above picture?

How many flowers are there in the above picture?

How many bees are there in the above picture?

How many trees are there in the above picture?

Date: _____   Teacher's Signature: _____

How Many Pairs?

The things in the two rows are related with each other. Observe them carefully and join them. One has been done for you.

1.

2.

3.

4.

a.

b.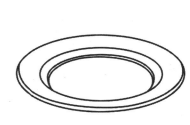

c.

d.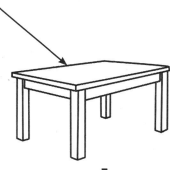

Now, tell how many pairs are there in total? _____

Date: _____

Teacher's Signature: _____

Mickey and Her Friend

Mickey, the fish, is searching for her friend Minnie, the starfish. Help her by following the correct path to reach Shiny.

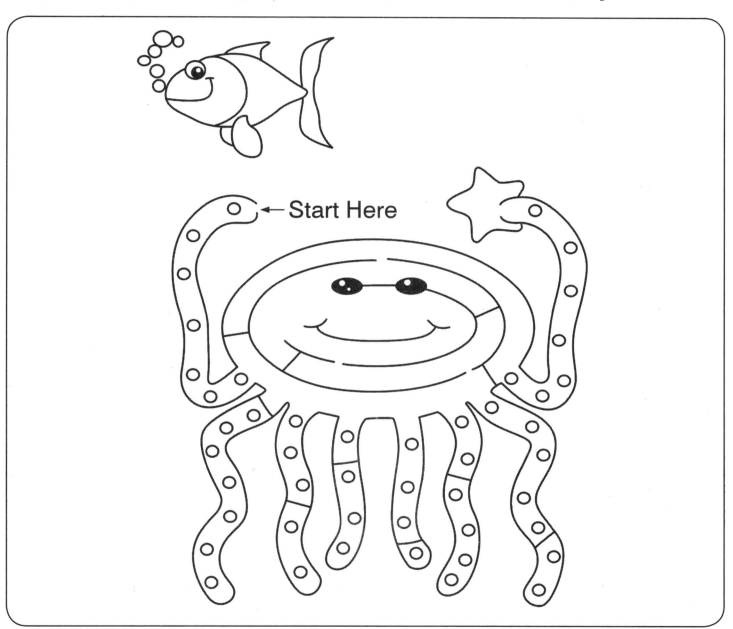

In the above maze you can observe one more water animal. Take help from your elders and write the name of the animal below.

It is an _____. It has _____ arms.

Date: _____   Teacher's Signature: _____

How Many Apples?

Count and fill in the boxes.

The total number of apple trees

The total number of apples

How many trees have three apples?

Match Us

Count the number of eggs and match them with the suitable number.

1

2

3

4

5

6

Date: _____

Teacher's Signature: _____

Spot the Differences

Find seven differences in the two pictures given below.

Least Number

Which of the following rows have the least number of things? Write the row number in the given box.

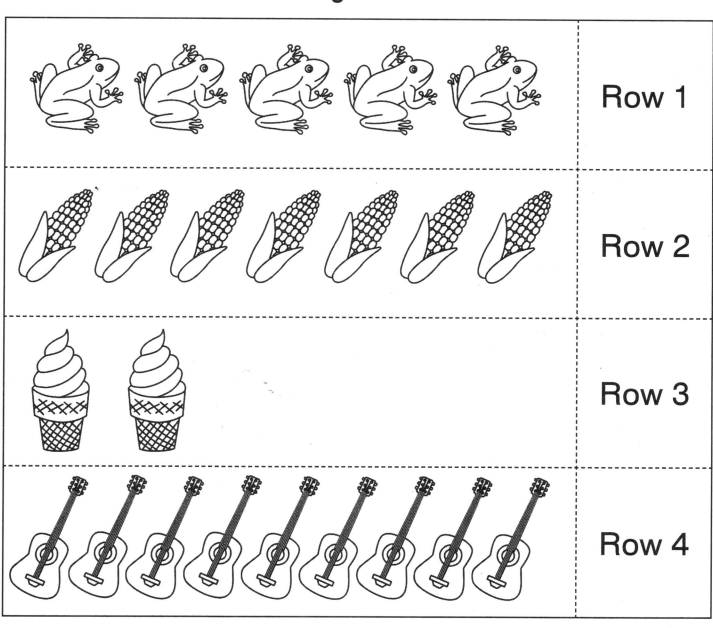

	Row 1
	Row 2
	Row 3
	Row 4

Row number ☐ has the least number of things.

Date: _____

Teacher's Signature: _____

Fruit or Vegetable?

Connect the dots from 1-10 and see what you get.

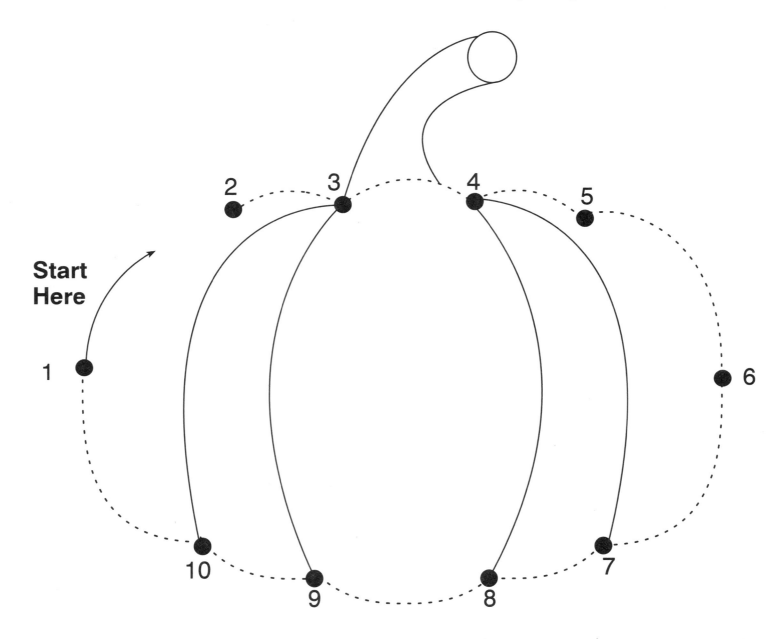

Start Here

Now, fill in the blanks.

I am a _____. (fruit/vegetable)

My name is _____.

Date: _____   Teacher's Signature: _____

Missing Element

Look at the pictures given below. Some elements are missing in one picture of every row. Draw the incomplete areas and colour all the pictures.

How many things are there in each row?

How many things are there in total?

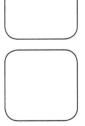

How Many Birds?

Look at the picture given below. Count the birds and baby birds in the picture.

The number of baby birds is_____.

The total number of birds is_____.

Small and Big

Look at the given pictures carefully. Colour the larger picture in each row.

Make the Graph

How many coconuts are there on the trees? Colour the spaces on the graph to show the total number of coconuts on the trees.

10	
9	
8	
7	
6	
5	
4	
3	
2	
1	■

Date: _____

Teacher's Signature: _____

No Joking

Match the two similar clowns and find out how many pairs are there. One has been done for you.

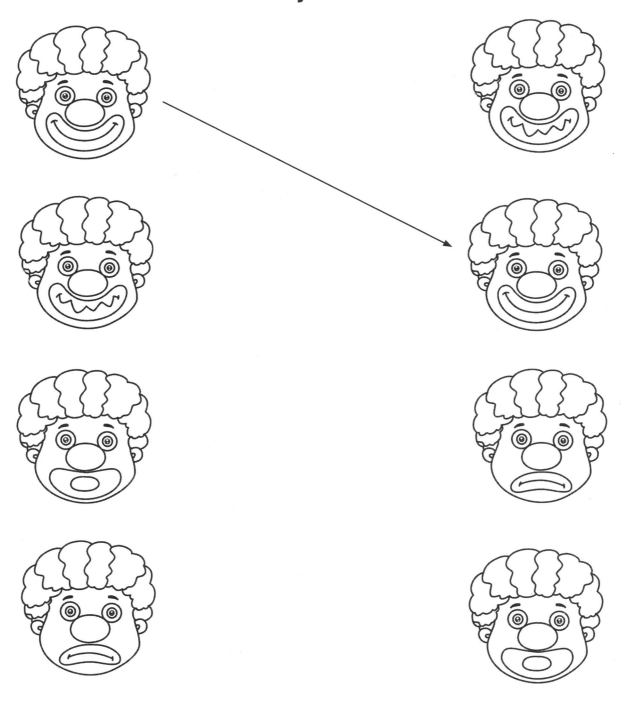

There are _____ pairs of clowns.

Count the Rings

Count the number of rings and other shapes given in the picture.

The number of rings is _____.

The number of other shapes is _____.

Date: _____

Teacher's Signature: _____

How Many Swans?

How many swans are swimming in the water?

The number of swans are_____.

Correct the Sequence

The following pictures are the steps for drawing a cat. But they are not in the correct order. Indicate numbers 1-4 for the right sequence.

Date: _____

Teacher's Signature: _____

Twin Teapots

Look at the pictures given below. Match the pairs of teapots and kettles. One has been done for you.

Phone Numbers

Write the phone numbers of your mother and father.

Mother

Father

Date: _____

Teacher's Signature: _____

Car Race

Look at the pictures given below. Write 1, 2, 3, 4, and 5 on the cars according to their position from the finish line.

FINISH

Date: _____

Teacher's Signature: _____

Big Versus Small

Write 'S' in front of the smallest number and 'B' in front of the biggest number in each row.

4	1	5	3	2

9	6	10	8	7

15	14	11	13	12

18	20	17	19	16

Date: _____

Teacher's Signature: _____

Correct Number

Count the things in the pictures and circle the correct number.

Number of trees   1   2   3   4   5

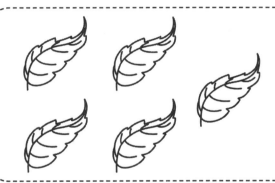

Number of leaves   1   2   3   4   5

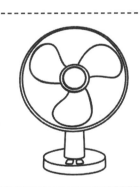

Number of fans   1   2   3   4   5

Number of shoes   1   2   3   4   5

Date: _____

Teacher's Signature: _____

Numbers and Train

Look at the picture of the train given below. Each dot shows a person inside it.

How many people are sitting in the first wagon of the train? _____

How many people are sitting in both the wagons of the train? _____

Date: _____

Teacher's Signature: _____

Striking the Number

Strike out the number that matches with the number of things in the box. One has been done for you.

3, ~~2~~, 5

2, 4, 5

2, 5, 3

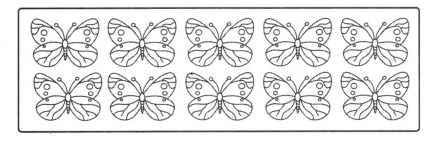

10, 9, 12

4, 7, 8

Date: _____   Teacher's Signature: _____

The Number List

Match the numbers with number names.

1	Ten
2	Five
3	Two
4	Eight
5	Seven
6	One
7	Three
8	Nine
9	Six
10	Four

Date: _____

Teacher's Signature: _____

Rhyme with Numbers

Match the sentences with the matching sound of the number names. One has been done for you.

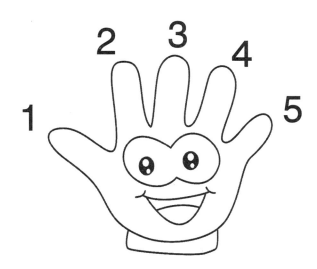

One   I am Free

Two   She is a bore

Three   Let's dive

Four   Look at the Sun

Five   Buckle your shoe

Trace and Colour

Trace the numbers and colour the tortoise.

Date: _____

Teacher's Signature: _____

How Many?

Count the body parts in the pictures given below.

I have _____ fingers.

I have _____ knees.

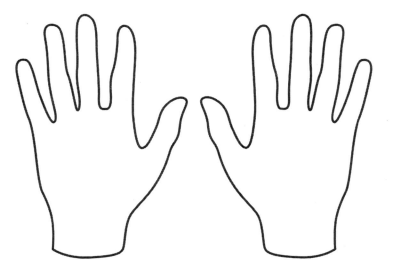

I have _____ elbows.

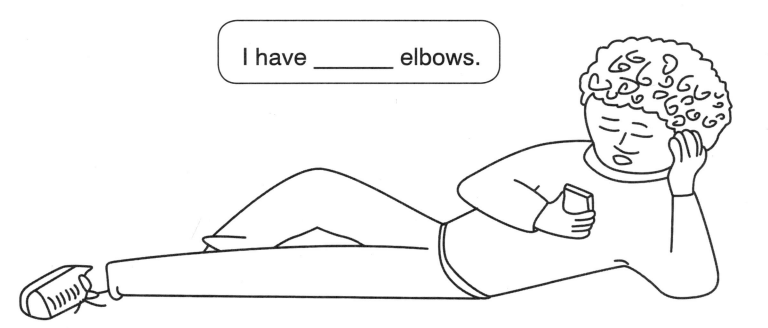

Hidden Number

Look at the picture given below. Identify its resemblance with the given numbers. Circle the correct answer.

| 9 | 10 | 12 | 11 |

Date: _____

Teacher's Signature: _____

Match the Petals

Count the number of petals. Tick mark (✓) the flower that has the same number of petals as the number given in between.

Hide and Seek

Identify the hidden number in the picture given below.

Hidden number is _____.

The insect crawling near it is _____.

Colour the Bear

Look at the picture carefully. There are numbers written on the picture of the bear. Read those numbers and colour them according to the Colour Key.

Colour Key

1 = Brown	2 = Yellow	3 = Red	4 = Blue

Date: _____

Teacher's Signature: _____

87 Worms and the Apples

Five worms are eager to eat the apples in the baskets. Each worm wants to eat one apple. Find out which basket has the right number of apples and colour it.

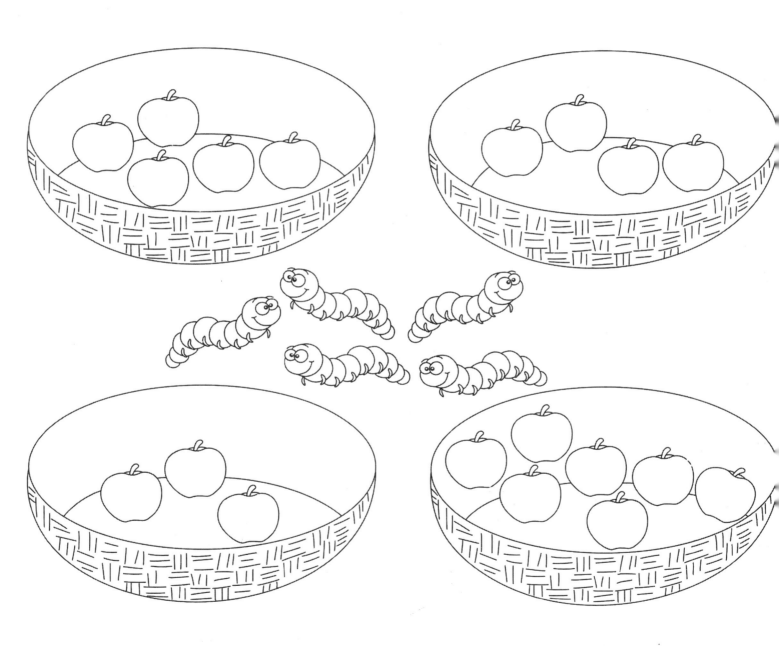

Date: _____

Teacher's Signature: _____

Groups of Three

Look at the picture given below. Tick (✓) the pictures that are three in number in a bunch. Now count the total number of bunches of three _____.

Tasty Fruits

Look at the fruits in the box given below. Colour the fruits. Count the total number of fruits in it.

The total number of fruits are_____.

Date: _____   Teacher's Signature: _____

Game of Shapes

Look at the pictures carefully. Count the number of similar shapes and write them.

How many shapes are there in total?

Same Number

Look at the pictures below. Count the objects in each group. Now draw a line and match the group with the same number of objects.

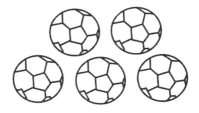

Fruits and Veggies

Count the total number of types of fruits and vegetables separately.

The number of types of fruits is _____.

The number of types vegetables is _____.

Date: _____   Teacher's Signature: _____

Size Matters

Look at the objects carefully. They are arranged from smallest to biggest in line. Write 1 in front of smallest object and 4 in front of biggest object in each row.

Date: _____

Teacher's Signature: _____

Mr Monkey and Lollipops

Mr. Monkey wants to reach the lollipops. But there are so many stones. Help him jump over them and reach the lollipops by jumping on odd numbered stones. Also, colour the odd numbered stones.

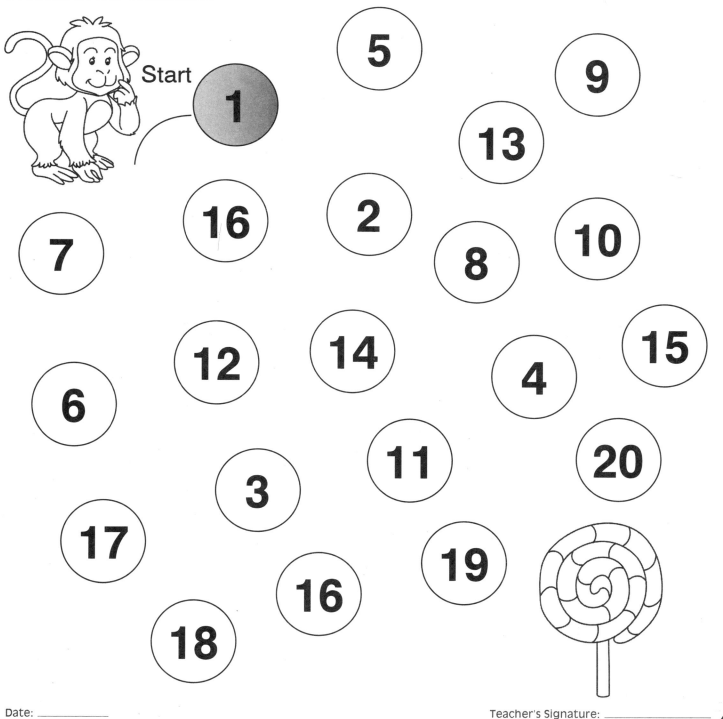

Date: _____   Teacher's Signature: _____

Shapes

Look at the shapes given below. Take help from your elders and write the names of these shapes in the given blank space.

Date: _____

Teacher's Signature: _____

Miss Bee

Help Miss Bee reach the flowers by creating a path by flying over even numbered crystals. Also, colour those even numbered crystals. Some crystals are shaded for your help. Put numbers from 1-30

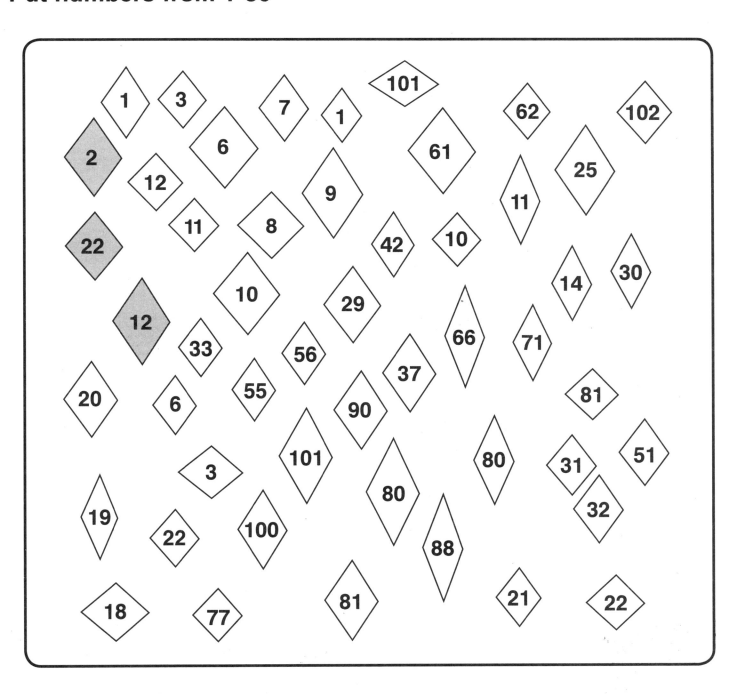

Shape Search

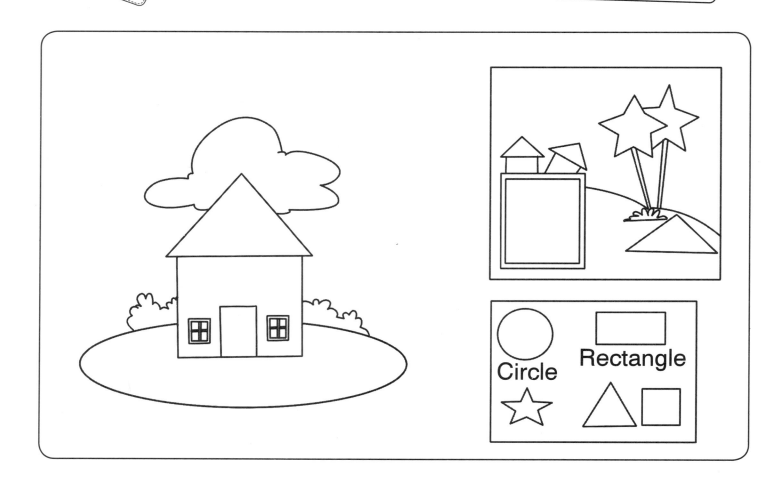

Count all the shapes you find in the above picture. Also write their number below.

Number of circles: _____.

Number of triangles: _____.

Number of squares: _____.

Number of rectangles: _____.

Number of stars: _____.

Date: _____   Teacher's Signature: _____

Busy Caterpillar

Ronny, the caterpillar is a very busy creature. He wants to complete the following counting table. Can you help him complete it?

1	2		4	5
6		8		10
11		13	14	
	17		19	20
21	22	23		25
	27		29	30

Date: _____

Teacher's Signature: _____

Mamma Sparrow

Help mamma sparrow to find the baby sparrows in the nest. Make a path through circle and squares only.

Start Here→

Date: _____

Teacher's Signature: _____

The World is Round

Tick mark (✓) all the circular objects given below.

 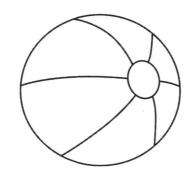 

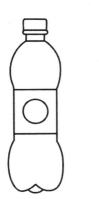 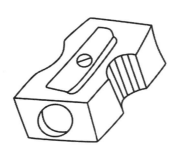 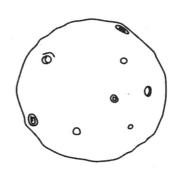

Now, complete the images given below.

Circles We Love

Colour all the circles in the following picture.

Date: _____

Teacher's Signature: _____

Do you know how many days are there in a week? Let's count and find out.

Write numbers in front of each day and find out the number of days in a week. Start from 1.

Monday	1
Tuesday	
Wednesday	
Thursday	
Friday	
Saturday	
Sunday	

Date: _____   Teacher's Signature: _____

Snowman needs his scarf to protect himself from the cold weather. Help him by following the correct path. Join the cap and the gloves only.

Date: _____   Teacher's Signature: _____

Odd One Out

Find the odd one out in the three lines below.

Example: a   (C)   b   d

Ist Line ⟹   **M**   **N**   **O**   **p**

IInd Line ⟹   **4**   **5**   **6**   **vii**

IIIrd Line ⟹

Date: _____   Teacher's Signature: _____

More or Less

Look at the food plates. One plate has more items than the others. Circle the plate that has more items.

Plate A

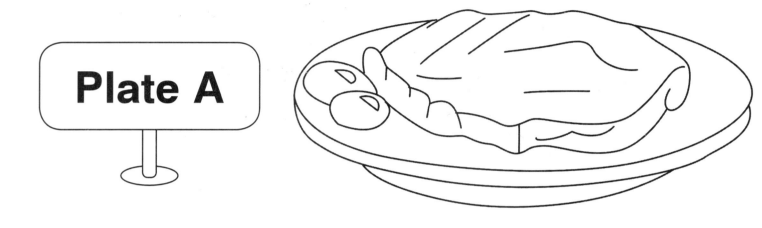

Plate B

Date: _____

Teacher's Signature: _____

Heavy and Light

Look at the pictures below. Answer the questions by putting the tick mark (✓) in the given boxes.

1. Which is heavier?

2. Which is lighter?

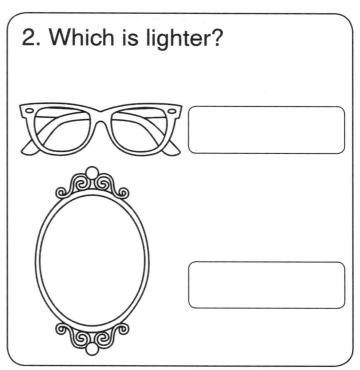

3. Which is heavier?

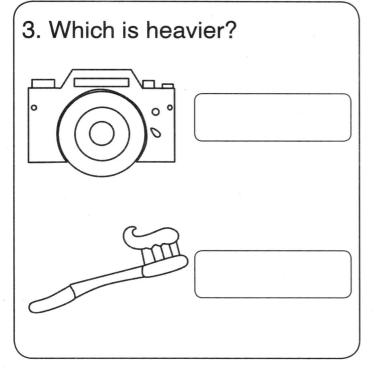

4. Which is lighter?

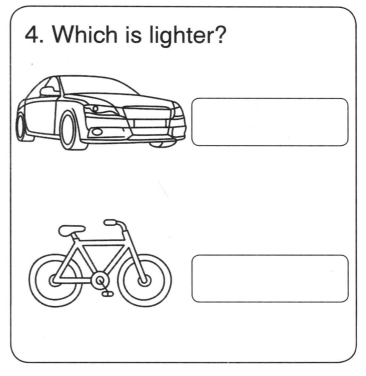

Date: _____

Hidden Shapes

Name the shapes in the given pictures and colour them.

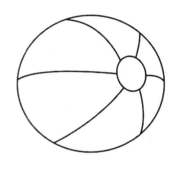

_____

_____

_____

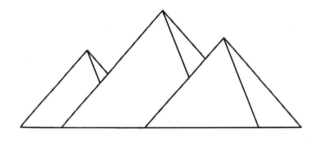

_____

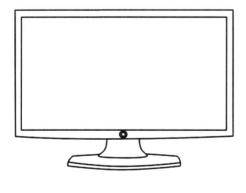

_____

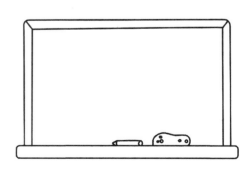

_____

The Shapes in Me

Match the shapes and complete the dotted images.

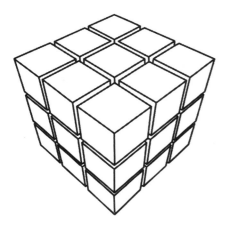

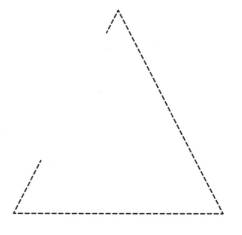

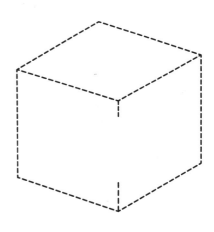

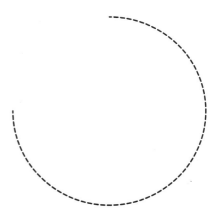

Match the Shapes

Look at the following shapes. They are incomplete. Match and complete the shapes.

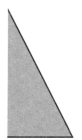

Who Am I?

Identify and count the total number of shapes. Get help from the Clue Box.

Shapes' names: _____

Total number of Shapes: ⬜

CLUE BOX

| circle | square | semicircle | rectangle |

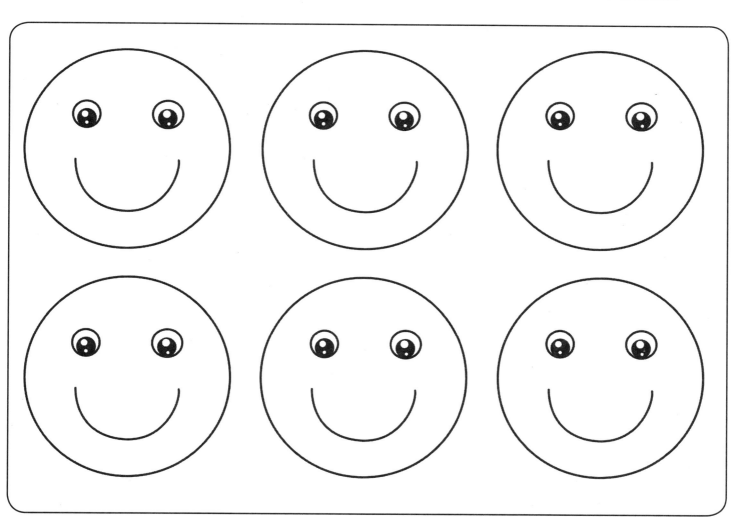

Legs Are Important

Look at the pictures given below. Count and write the number of legs in each picture in the boxes.

Date: _____

Teacher's Signature: _____

Odd one Out

Colour the odd one out in the following.

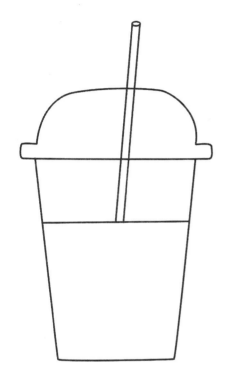

Making a Snowman

Give the correct order for steps to make a snowman. Write 1 for first, 2 for second and 3 for third in the given boxes.

Date: _____

Teacher's Signature: _____

Pattern Creation

Use the given fruits and arrange them in four different ways. Create your own patterns. One pattern has been created for you.

1.

2.

3.

4.

Sheep in a Farm

Sally saw three groups of sheep in a farm. Help her count the sheep in the groups and then add them. Also, find out the total number of sheep.

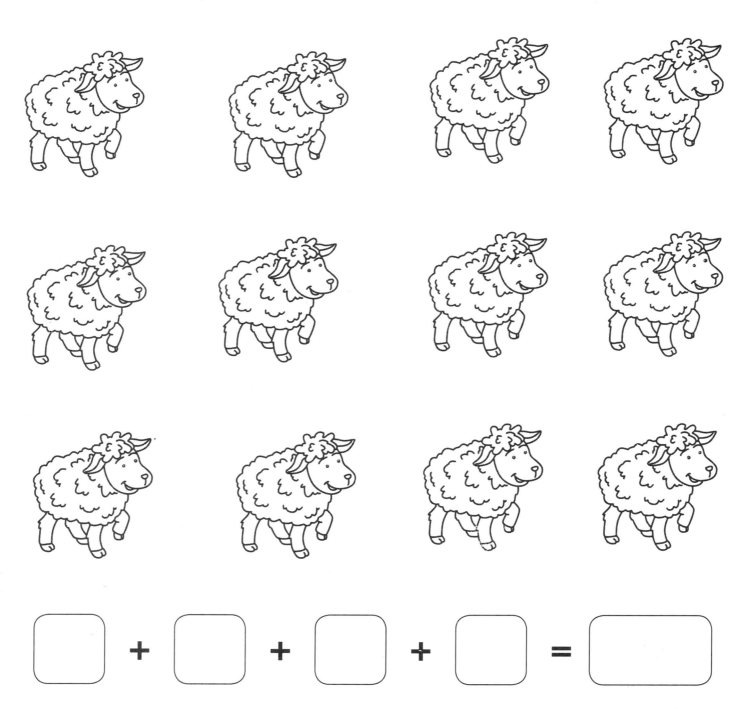

$$\boxed{} + \boxed{} + \boxed{} + \boxed{} = \boxed{}$$

Date: _____

Teacher's Signature: _____

Santa's Gifts

On Christmas Day, Santa brought several gifts for little Pennie. Pennie gave some gifts to her friends and cousins. How many gifts does she have now?

1.  − =

 − =

2.  −  =

 − =

3.  −  =

 − =

Date: _____

Teacher's Signature: _____

How Many?

Look at the given picture carefully. Count and write the number of similar objects.

 _____

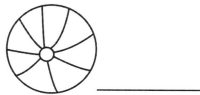 _____

_____

Date: _____

Teacher's Signature: _____

Shape Jumble

Colour the ⬤ orange, the ▷ red and the ▢ blue.

Oval Not Circle

Look at the pictures given below. Identify the oval shape in each picture. Count and write the number of ovals in each picture.

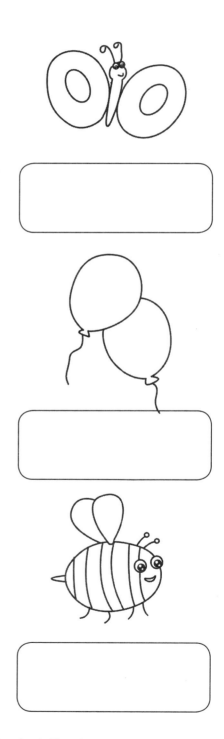

Date: _____

Teacher's Signature: _____

Hidden Balloons!

Colour the spaces with the two digit numbers in any colour to find out all of the hidden balloons.

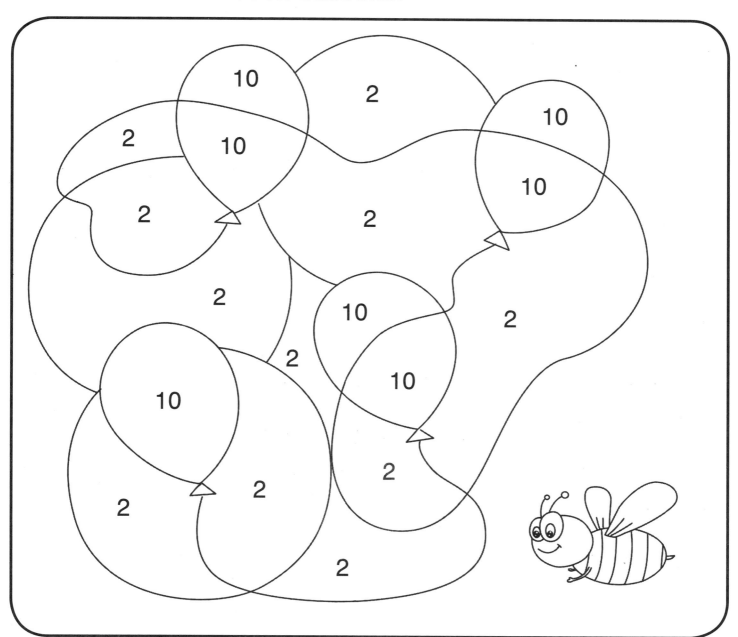

Can you count how many two-digit numbers are there in the picture?

Smiling Grapes

Count and write the total number of the bunches of grapes _____.

Count and write the total number of smiling grapes _____.

Date: _____

Teacher's Signature: _____

Myra and Kaira

Identify Myra and Kaira in the pictures with the help of the given clues.

Myra has a smaller family than Kaira. Myra has a younger brother. Kaira has two younger brothers.

Who Is Small?

All the things around us have different shapes and sizes. Some are big while some are small. There are two animals in the picture given below. Write 'Big' in front of the big animal and 'Small' in front of the small animal:

Which animal is inside a cage? _____

Date: _____

Teacher's Signature: _____

Odd Shapes

Look at the pictures given below. There is one odd shape among all. Find out that odd figure and put a cross (x) in the given box.

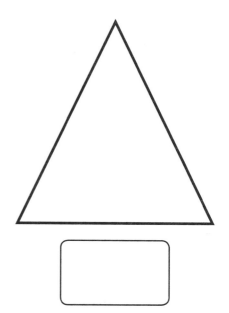

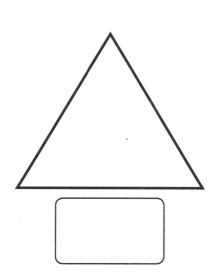

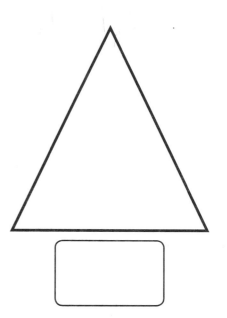

Arrange in Order

Arrange the following activities in the order in which they are done daily by numbering 1-5.

_____

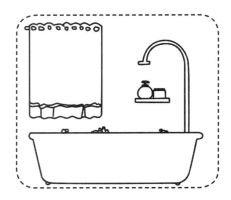

_____

_____

_____

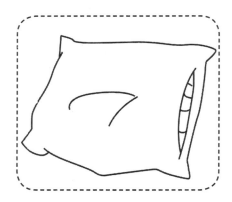

_____

Sequencing

Look at the pictures given below and arrange them correctly by writing numbers below them.

In a Playground

Suzy loves to play in a playground. Look at the picture given below. Count and write the number of objects that are related to the playground.

Number of objects related to the playground are: _____.

Morning-Evening-Night

Write morning, evening, and night in front of every picture given below. Do you do these things? At what time do you do these activities? Write down the time.

Before and After

Fill in the missing numbers. One has been done for you.

Before	Between	After
4	5	6
	7	
	3	
	8	
	9	
	2	

Date: _____

Teacher's Signature: _____

Andy went out to play. He saw many Lego blocks with different letters written on them. Circle the block with the highest number of letters.

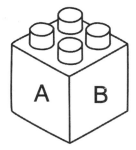

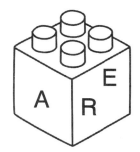

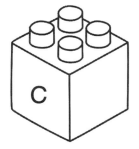
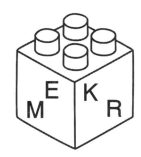
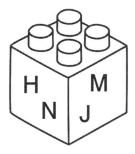
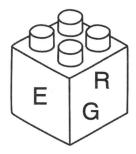

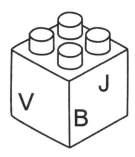
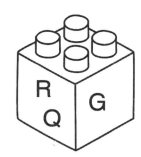
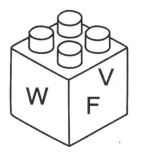
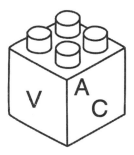

Date: _____

Teacher's Signature: _____

Match My Spots

Little beetles lost their spots. Help them to find their spots by matching them correctly. One has been done for you.

CLUE BOX

Small beetle has less spots while big beetle has more spots.

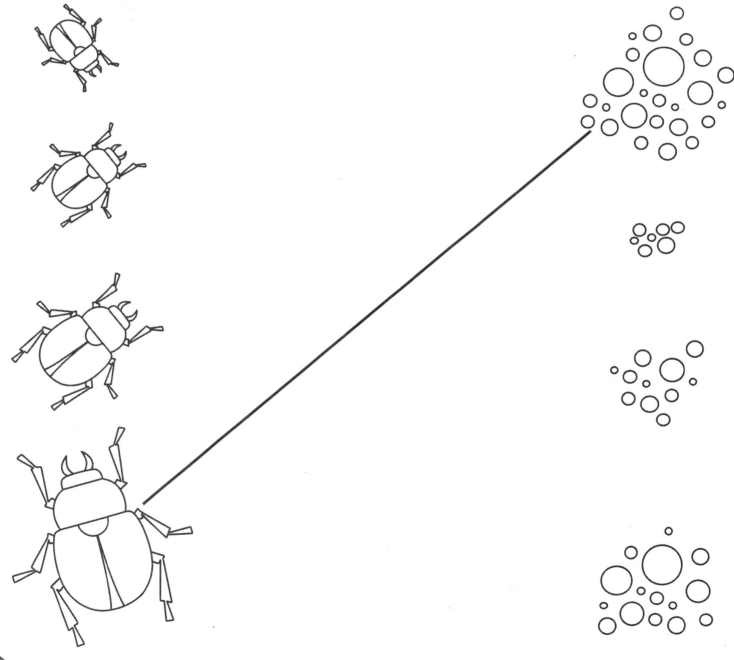

Date: _____

Teacher's Signature: _____

Left and Right

Look at the pictures given below and answer the questions that follow.

Total number of penguins: _____

Number of penguins turning right: _____

Number of penguins turning left: _____

Date: _____

Teacher's Signature: _____

Name and Numbers

Look at the picture given below. First identify the animal and then count them. Take help from the Clue Box.

ANIMAL CLUE BOX

bee	ant	beetle

NUMBER CLUE BOX

4	5	6	8	10

Name of the animal: _____

Number of animals: _____

Date: _____

Teacher's Signature: _____

I Am Different

Look at the pictures given below. In each row, there is one picture, which is different from all others. Identify the different picture and put a tick mark (✓) in front of that image.

More or Less

Look at the shapes in each box and colour the group that has more number of shapes.

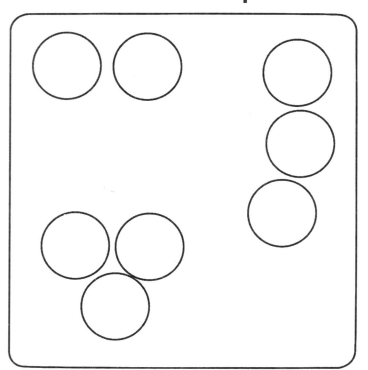

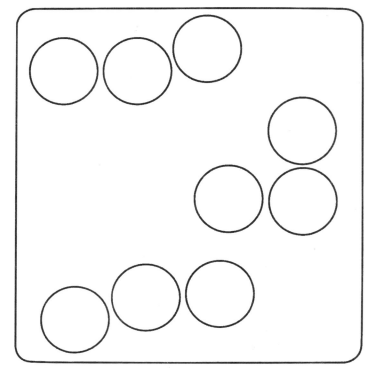

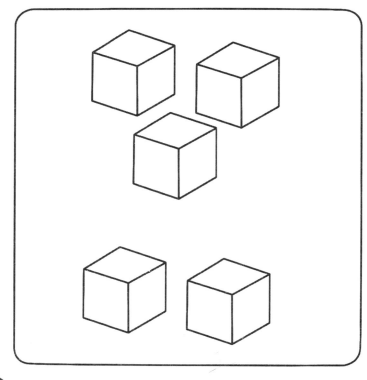

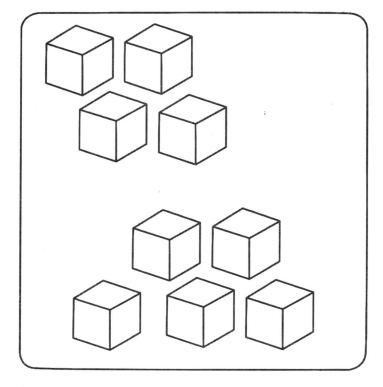

Date: _____

Teacher's Signature: _____

Bigger or Smaller

Look at the things in each box, and circle the smaller ones.

Pick the Right Number

Count the number of objects in each box. Match the right number for each box.

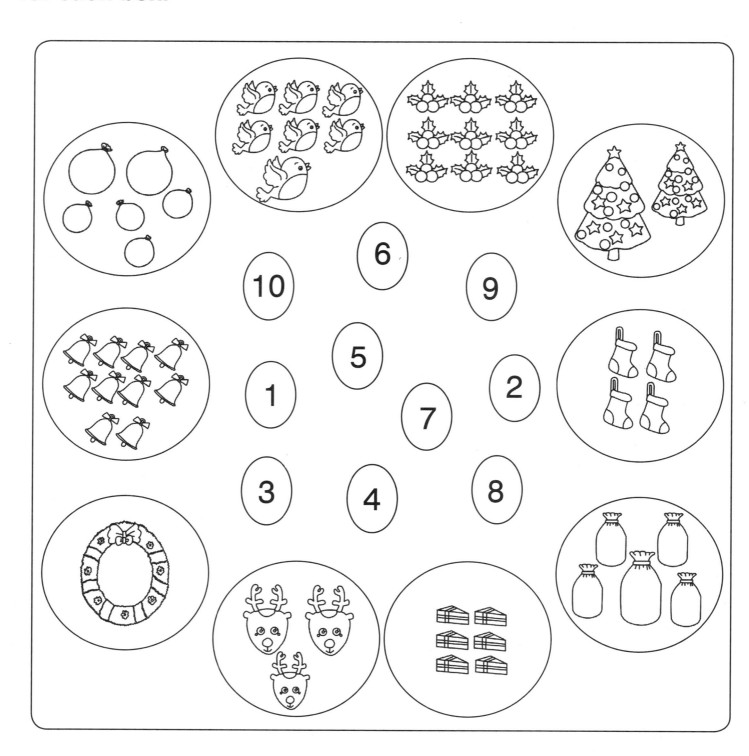

Date: _____

Teacher's Signature: _____

Caps and Hats

Pam's mother went to the market and bought some caps and hats. Look at them and answer the questions that follow.

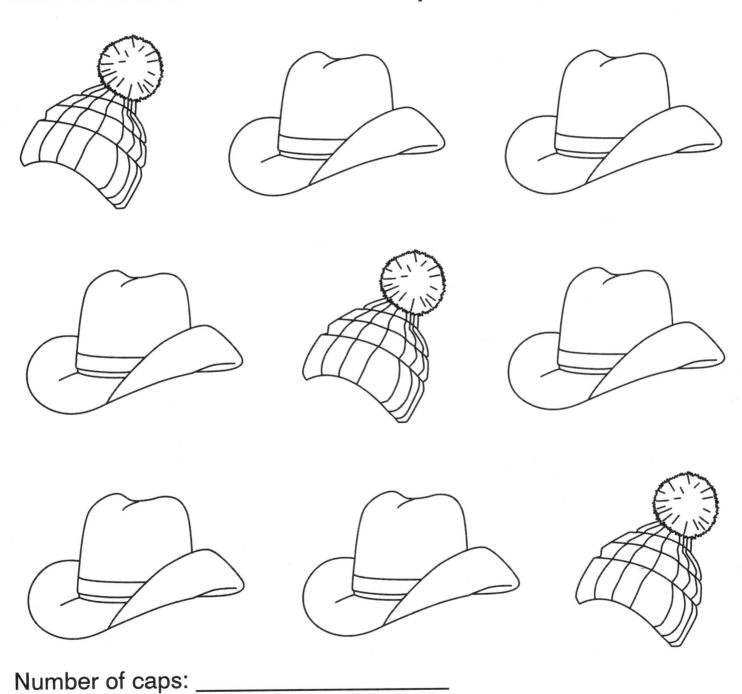

Number of caps: _____

Number of hats: _____

Let's Count and Add

Count and add the objects and then write their total number in the given boxes.

A.  **+**  **=**

 **+** **=** **+**

B.  **+**  **=**

 **+** **=** **+**

C. **+** **=**

 **+** **=**

Playtime!

Maria went to the playground. She saw so many things there. Look at them and answer the questions that follow.

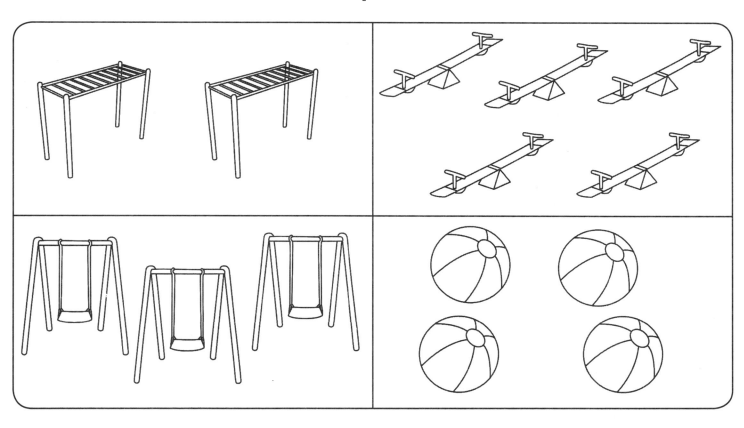

How many monkey bars are there?

How many seesaws are there?

How many swings are there?

How many balls are there?

Date: _____

Teacher's Signature: _____

In School

There are so many things kept together. Circle the things, which belong to school.

How many round objects are there in the box? _____

How many clothes are there in the box? _____

Date: _____   Teacher's Signature: _____

Insects and Animals

Look at the pictures given below and circle the insects in them.

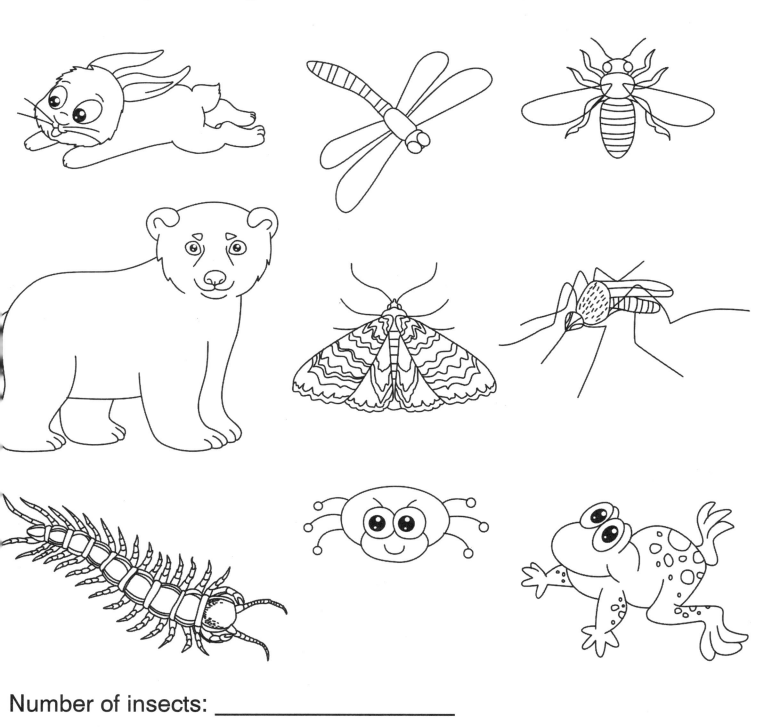

Number of insects: _____

Number of animals: _____

Date: _____

Teacher's Signature: _____

Look at each set of pictures given below. It follows a pattern. What should be the next picture as per the pattern? Right the name of that picture.

1.

2.

3.

4.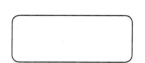

In the Garden

Join the dots from 1 to 12 and colour to find out who is fluttering in the garden.

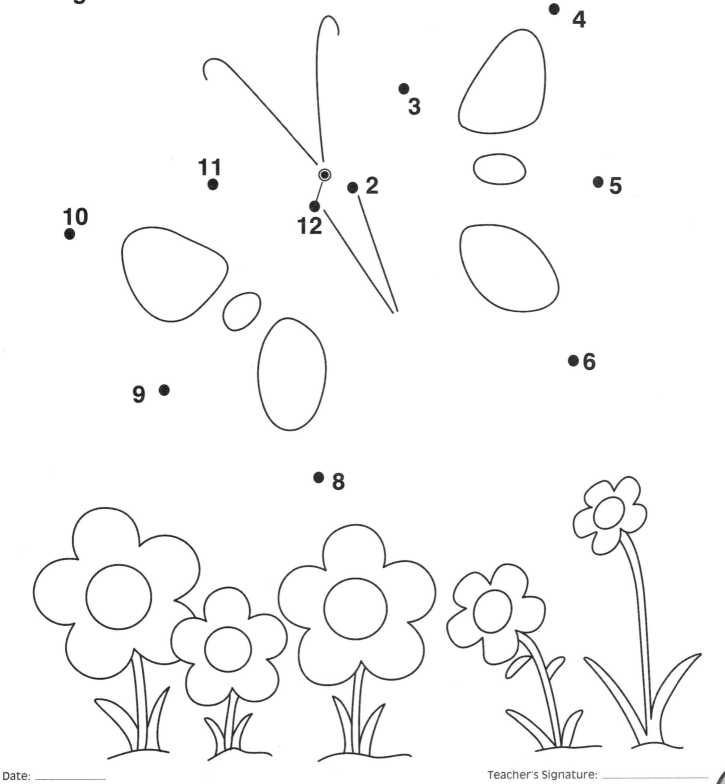

Who Am I?

Find out the name of the fish shown in the picture below. Trace the number of fish as given.

Date: _____

Teacher's Signature: _____

I Do Not Need Electricity

Look at the pictures given below. Some objects need electricity to work but some do not need electricity. Circle the things that do not need electricity to work. Also write the shape to which each object resemble. Take help of your parents.

I Am Yellow in Colour

Colour and count the following fruits and circle the ones that are yellow in colour. Total number of fruits:_____

How many fruits will be left in the box if you remove all the yellow fruits?

_____

Date: _____

Teacher's Signature: _____

Help Me

Rick is playing badminton. But he lost his shuttlecock. Help him find his shuttlecock by following the correct path, using arrows.

Where Is My Home?

It is raining. Little Maria wants to reach her home. Help her by following the right path towards her home.

Start Here

In the above maze, you can observe an object which we use in rainy season. Identify the object.

The object is an _____.

Compare

Look at the pictures given below. All three are of different sizes. Write 'T' for the tallest and 'S' for the smallest thing.

L

E

N

G

T

H

_____

_____

_____

Date: _____   Teacher's Signature: _____

Flower Path

Beauty the butterfly is searching for her favourite flower. Help her by following the correct path. Also identify the number in the path._____

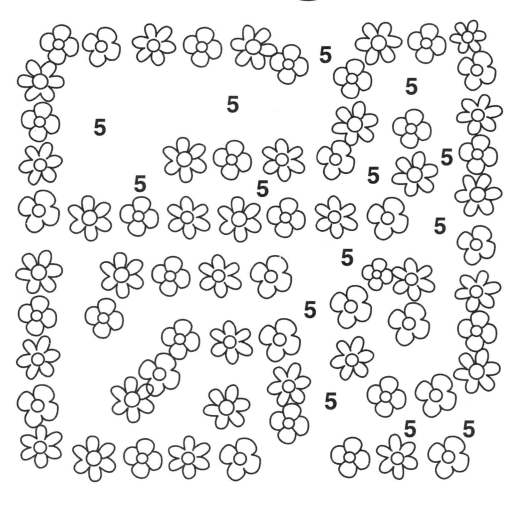

Date: _____   Teacher's Signature: _____

Big and Small

Some animals are small and some are big. Look at the pictures given below. Write 'S' in front of small and write 'B' in front of big.

Pat the Frog

Pat has lost the way to the pond. Help him find the way by following numbers 1-10.

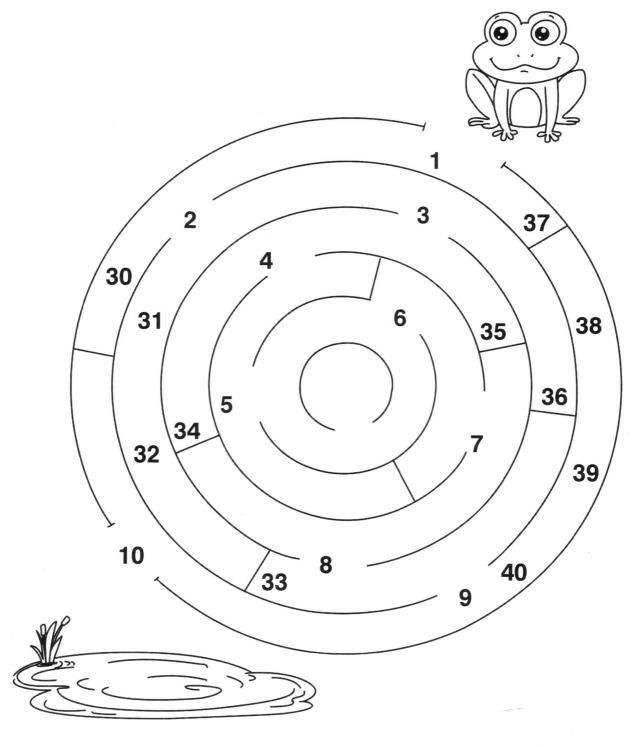

Date: _____

Teacher's Signature: _____

Draw the Shape

Can you draw the following shapes? You can take help from your parents.

Circle   Triangle   Star

Square   Rectangle   Diamond

Date: _____   Teacher's Signature: _____

Square, Square

Look at the picture given below. How many squares can you find in the picture?

Number of squares = _____

Date: _____

Teacher's Signature: _____

Trace and Identify

Trace the picture given below and identify the object with the help of the Clue Box.

_____

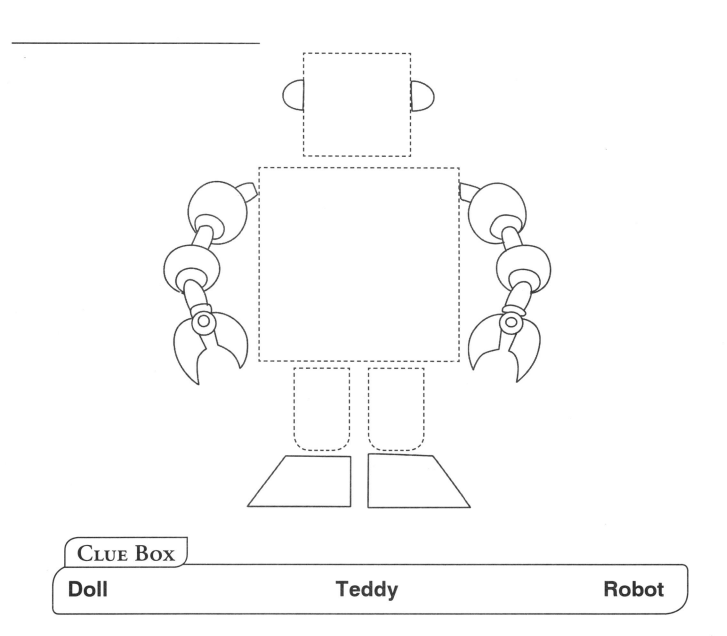

CLUE BOX

| **Doll** | **Teddy** | **Robot** |

How many different shapes are used to make this picture?

_____

Count Us

Look at the picture given below. It has so many shapes.
Count the number of triangles, squares and circles.

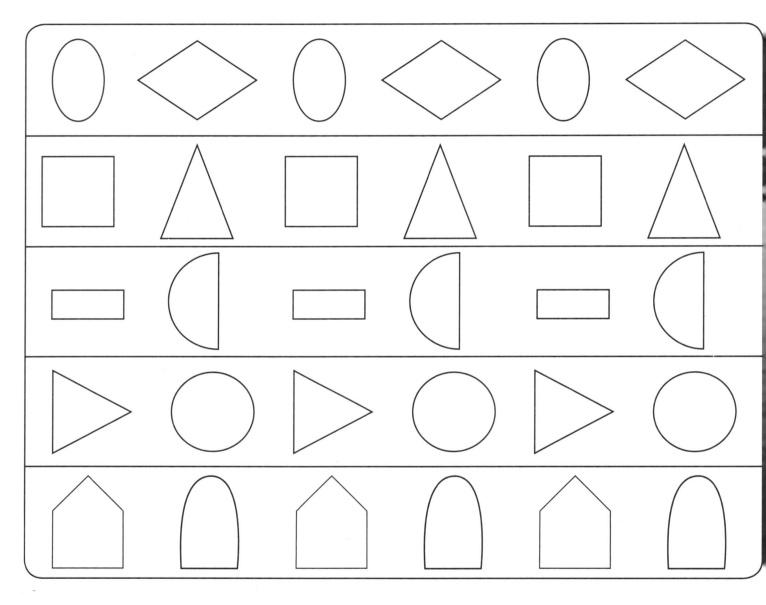

Number of triangles   = _____

Number of squares   = _____

Number of circles   = _____

Date: _____   Teacher's Signature: _____

I Am Not a Square!

Colour all the objects that are not squares.

Have you ever seen diamond-shaped objects?

A kite has a diamond shape. Let us trace and practice to draw a kite.

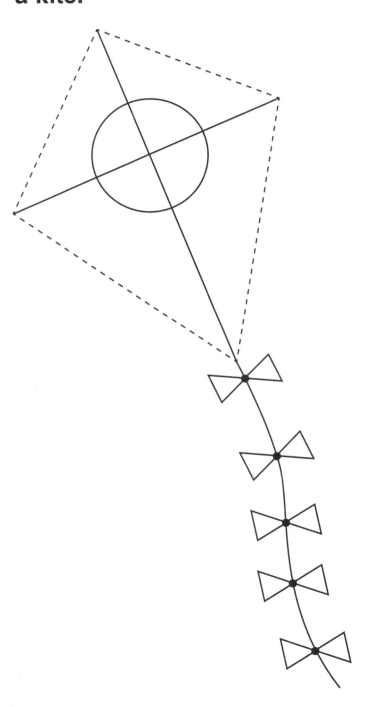
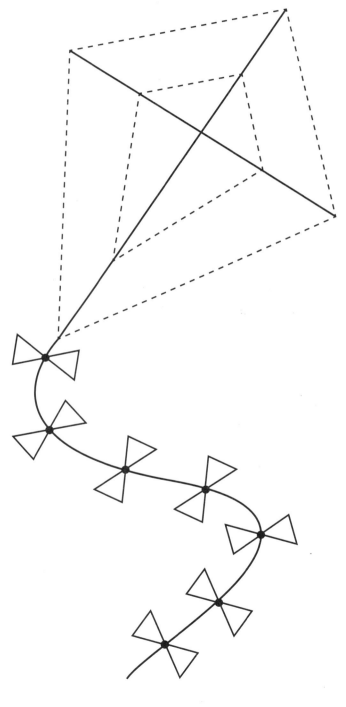

Date: _____

Teacher's Signature: _____

A Little Different!

Look at the pictures given below. Draw same pictures in the given spaces but they should have different heights than the existing ones.

- -

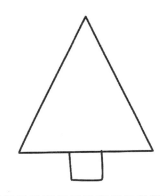

- -

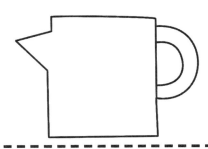

- -

Date: _____   Teacher's Signature: _____

A Little Smaller!

Look at the pictures given below. Draw same pictures in the given spaces. They should be smaller than the existing ones.

- -

- -

- -

Date: _____

Teacher's Signature: _____

My House

Little Kitten wants to build a house for herself. But she is confused how to complete it. Help her to complete her house using shapes from Help Box.

Help Box

square   circle   rectangle   triangle

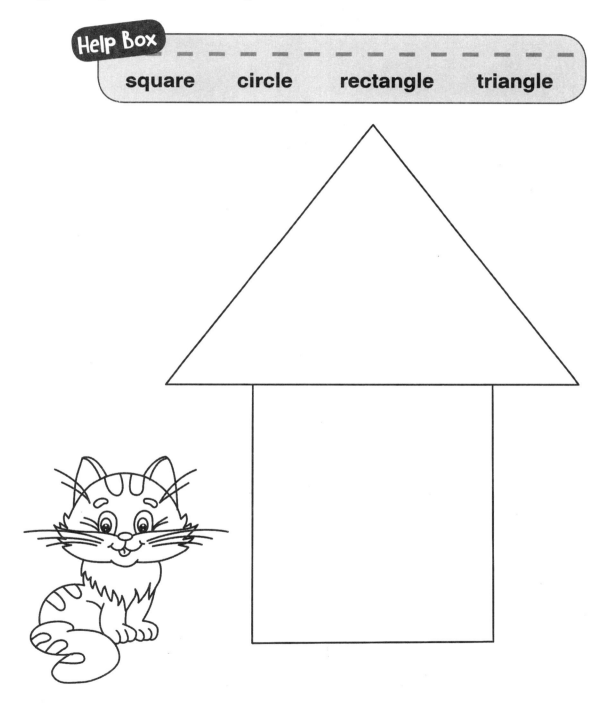

Date: _____

Teacher's Signature: _____

Add Up!

The lights are out. How many candles are being used? Count the candles and write the answer.

1 + 2 =

Date: _____

Teacher's Signature: _____

Great Fall

One Humpty-Dumpty fell off the wall! Count and write how many are still sitting on the wall?

Jumping Tom!

Toms' pet monkey is very naughty and ran away. Help Tom catch his pet by jumping on the stones. Use arrows to mark his path.

Date: _____

Teacher's Signature: _____

Highest Number

Which of the following row has the highest number of things? Write the number of the row in the given box.

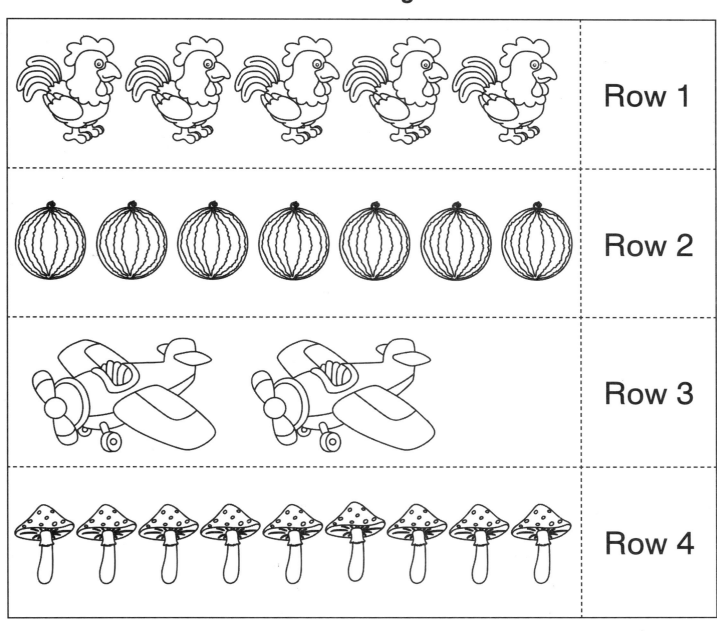

	Row 1
	Row 2
	Row 3
	Row 4

Row [   ] has the highest number of things.

Number Trouble

Look at the picture carefully. Some numbers are missing from each row. Fill in the missing numbers in each row.

Date: _____

Teacher's Signature: _____

Farm House

Mac's dad has a farmhouse. Look at the following pictures and identify and count the number of animals with the help of the Clue Box.

CLUE BOX		
two	eight	ten

Mac's father has total number of _____ animals.

Number of horses is _____.

Number of chickens is _____.

Making Squares

Connect the dots to create squares.

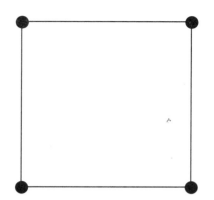

Date: _____

Teacher's Signature: _____

Balloons in the Sky

Look at the balloons and answer the questions that follow.

A.  —

B.  +

C.  +

D.  —

Balloons in row A   _____

Balloons in row B   _____

Balloons in row C   _____

Balloons in row D   _____

Date: _____   Teacher's Signature: _____

Straight Line

Look at the pictures given below. Some of the pictures are created with the help of straight and slanting lines ◹. Circle them.

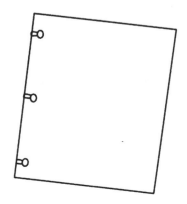

Date: _____

Teacher's Signature: _____

How Many Sides?

See the shape. It has four sides.

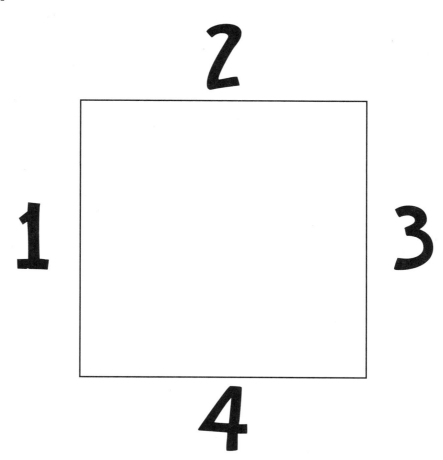

Find out the number of sides in the shapes given below.

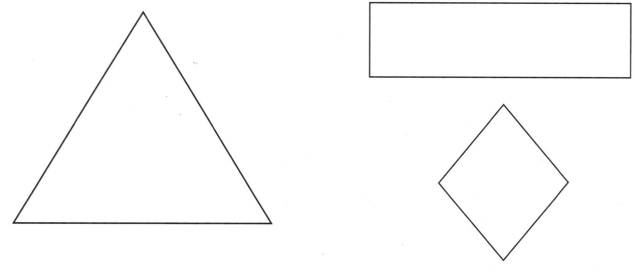

Naughty Rex

Rex burst many balloons at his friend Jack's birthday party.

Count the number of balloons that he did not burst. One has been done for you.

$$4 - 3 = 1$$

$$\boxed{} - \boxed{} = \boxed{}$$

$$\boxed{} - \boxed{} = \boxed{}$$

$$\boxed{} - \boxed{} = \boxed{}$$

My Clothing Hanger

With the help of the ruler given below measure each clothing.
Write the number of divisions in the box under them.

Circle the shortest clothing with a blue crayon.
Circle the longest clothing with a red crayon.

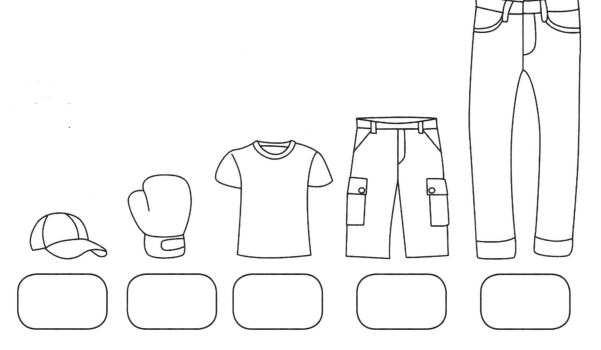

Find the answer of each sum and then use the answers (numbers) to colour the picture.

6 + 3 = _____ Black   2 + 3 = _____ Blue

4 + 2 = _____ Orange   5 + 2 = _____ Yellow

2 + 2 = _____ Green   2 + 1 = _____ Red

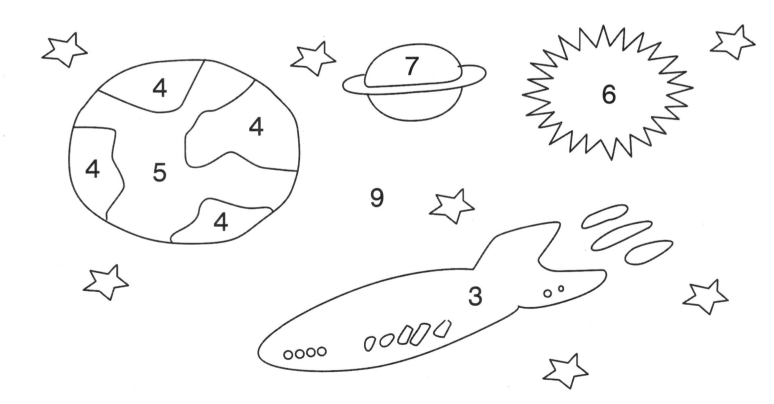

How Many Are Left?

Subtract the crossed out pictures and write the remaining number of things in the blank boxes.

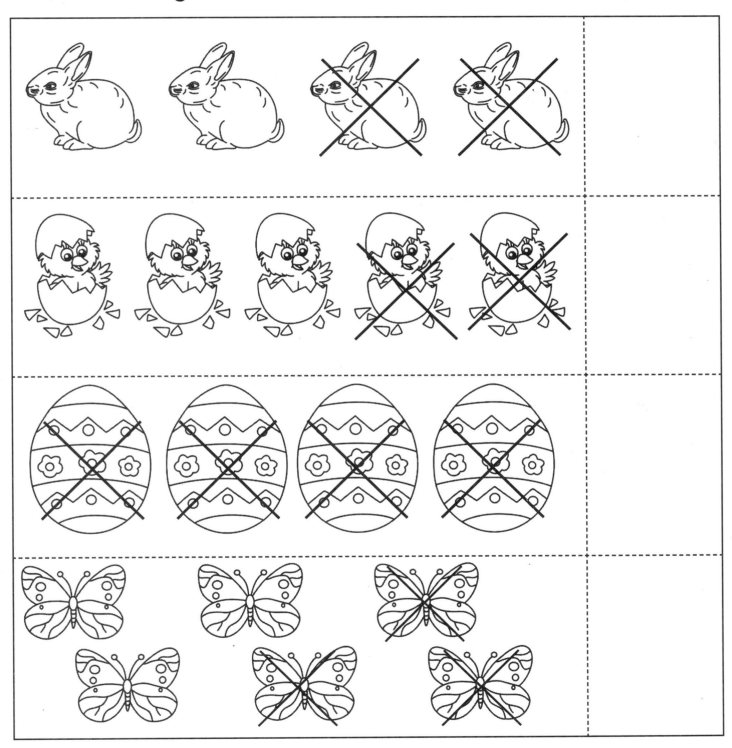

How Many Are Added?

Add and find out the total number of things in the boxes. Write the answer in the blank box.

Date: _____

Teacher's Signature: _____

Complete the Story!

Today, Mamma birdie is very happy because soon the chicks will hatch from her eggs. But, one day a naughty monkey came and destroyed two eggs out of five.

Now there are only _____ eggs remaining in Mamma birdie's nest.

Count the eggs in the nest to solve the problem.

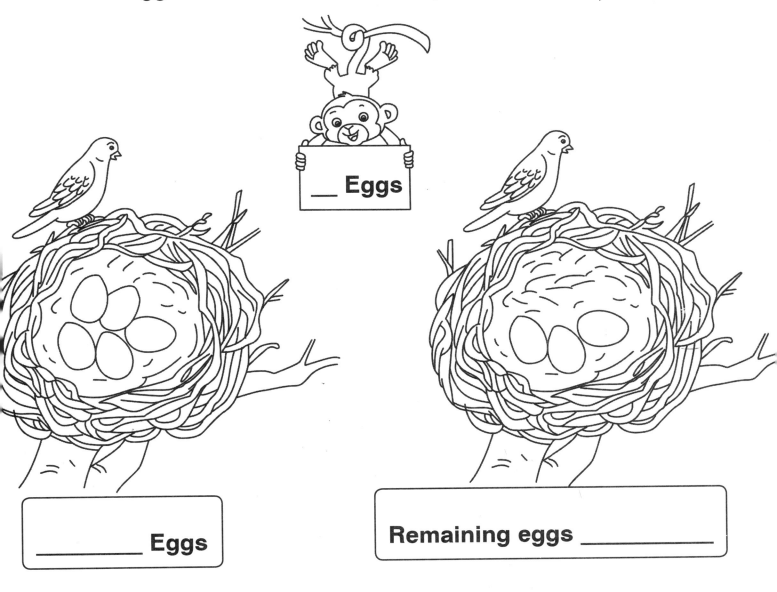

__ Eggs

_____ Eggs

Remaining eggs _____

Count and Fill

Amelia brought 30 eggs. Now she wants to reconfirm the number of eggs. Help her by counting from 1-30 and fill the missing numbers.

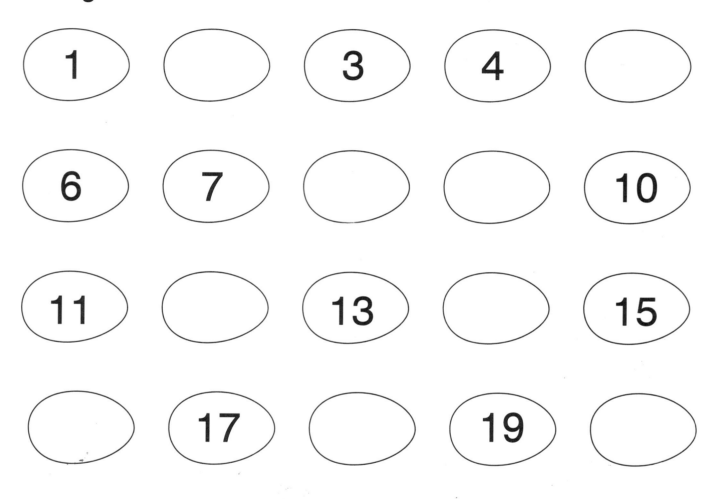

1   ☐   3   4   ☐

6   7   ☐   ☐   10

11   ☐   13   ☐   15

☐   17   ☐   19   ☐

21   ☐   23   ☐   25

☐   27   ☐   29   ☐

Date: _____

Teacher's Signature: _____

Identify and Count

Look at the picture given below. Circle the big flowers and count them.

Number of big flowers is: _____.

Date: _____

Identify and Count

Look at the picture given below. It is a collection of fruits and vegetables. Count and write the number of carrots.

Number of carrots is: _____.

Date: _____

Teacher's Signature: _____

Count the Footballs

Look at the picture given below. Count and write the number of footballs.

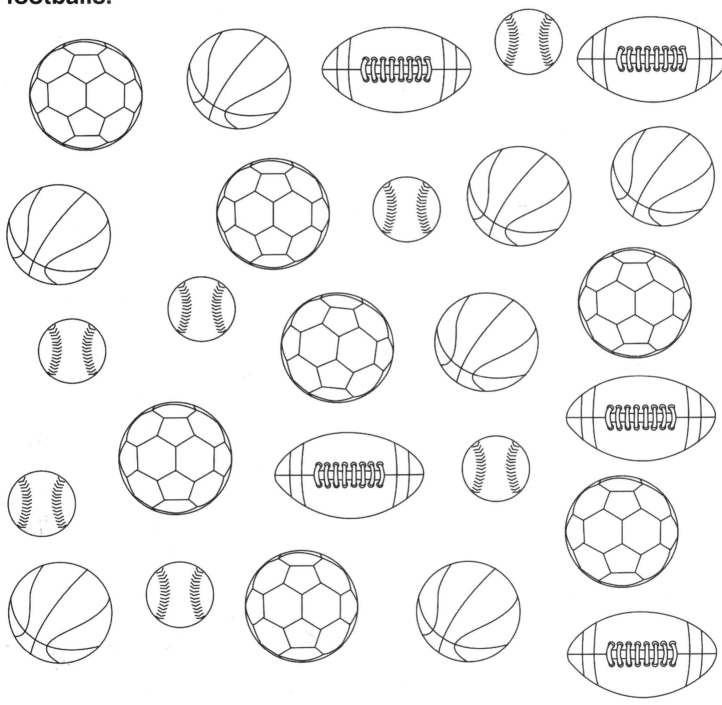

Number of footballs is: _____.

Date: _____

Teacher's Signature: _____

Shapes and Objects

Match the shapes with similar objects. One has been done for you.

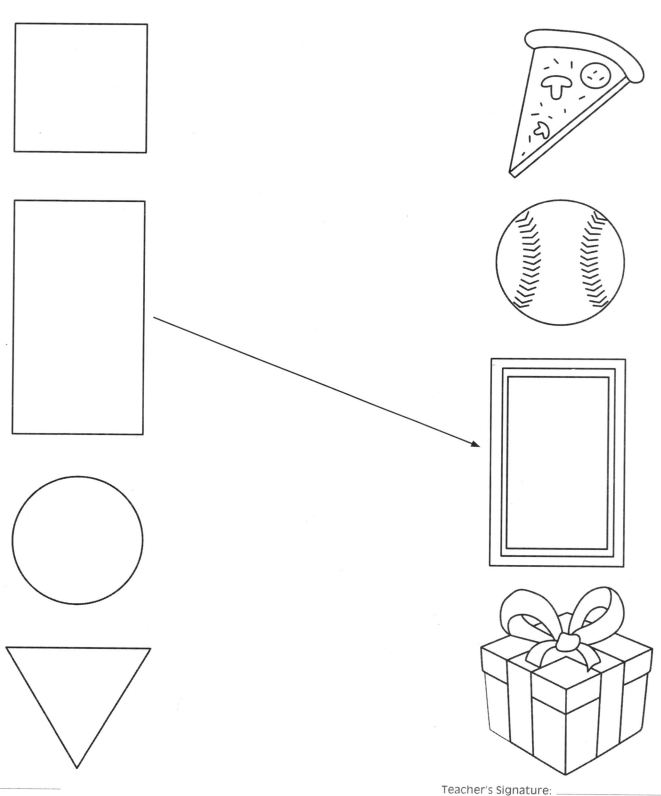

Date: _____

Teacher's Signature: _____

Odd One Out

Circle the odd one out in each of the following groups. The first one has been done.

1.

2.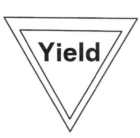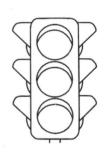

3.

4.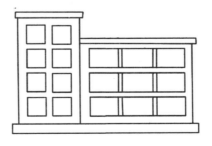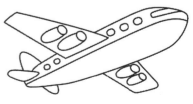

Date: _____

Teacher's Signature: _____

Making Pairs

How many pairs of different things can you find in the picture given below? Join them with a red line.

Tough Task

Identify the objects and count them. Write the number in the boxes given.

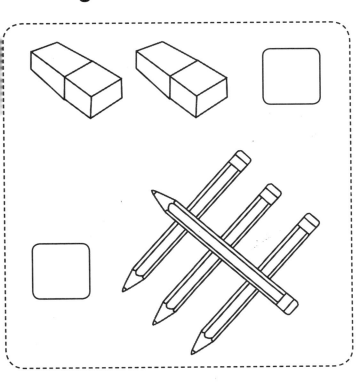

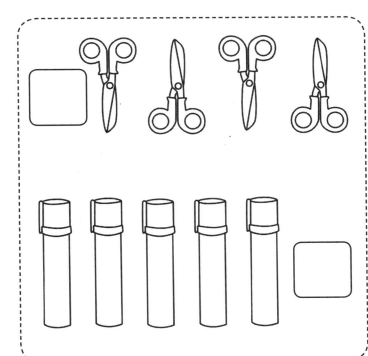

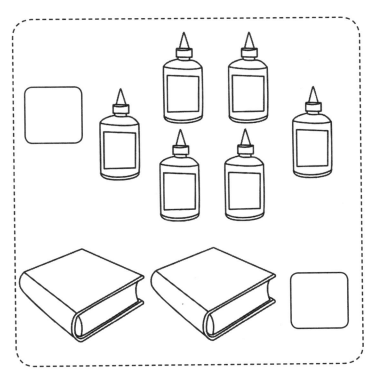

Are We all Same?

Look at the pictures given below. These are socks. Count how many different types of designs are there.

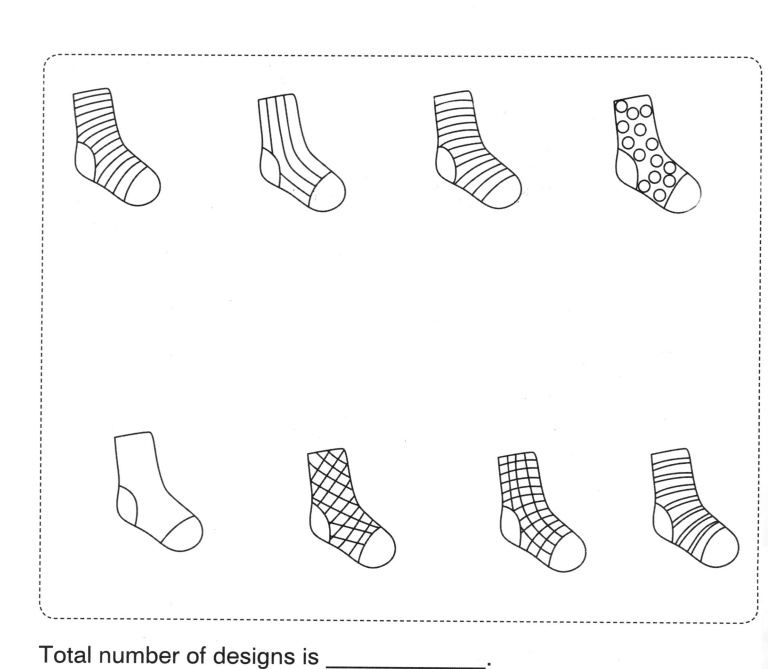

Total number of designs is _____.

Girls in a Queue

Look at the pictures given below. Circle the name of the girl standing at 3rd position from the right.

Left   Right

Daisy   Pretty   Jill   Kristine   Sammie

Date: _____   Teacher's Signature: _____

Counting Shapes

Look at the shapes given below and count them.

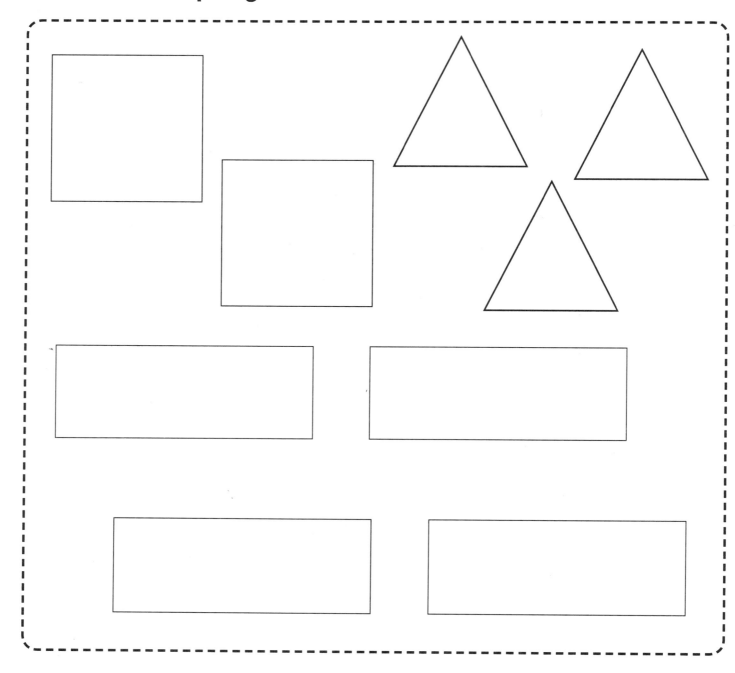

Total number of shapes: _____

Count the total number of straight lines in the shapes: _____

Date: _____

Teacher's Signature _____

What Comes Before Me?

Count the number of giraffes. Now strike out one giraffe from each box and count the remaining. Write that number in the bracket.

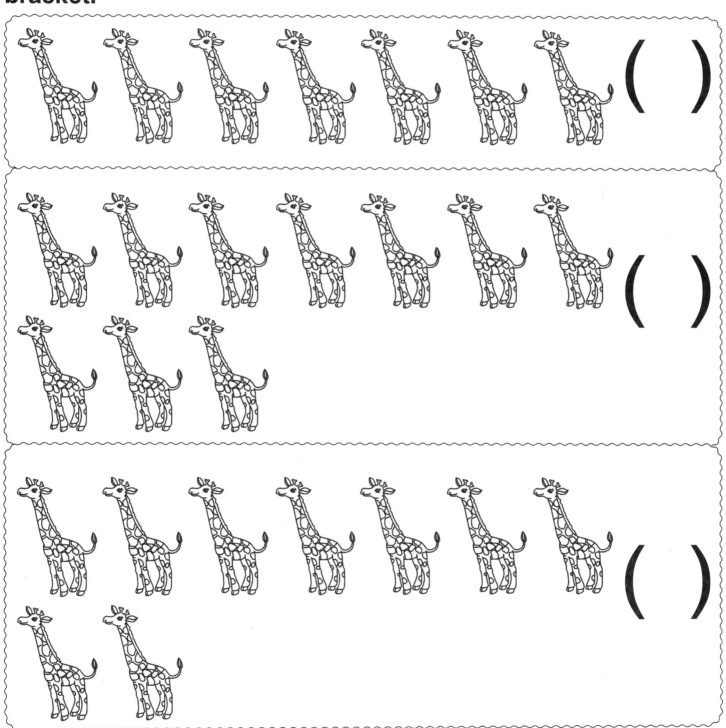

Decoding the Colour Key

Solve the sum given below the chick and colour the chick according to the Colour Key. For example, if your answer is 2, then colour the chick with red colour.

Colour Key

2 = Red	3 = Yellow	4 = Green	5 = Black

1 + 1 = ☐

2 + 1 = ☐

3 + 1 = ☐

3 + 0 = ☐

2 + 2 = ☐

2 + 0 = ☐

2 + 3 = ☐

4 + 1 = ☐

1 + 3 = ☐

Date: _____

Teacher's Signature: _____